The Ultimate Mediterranean Refresh Cookbook 2024

Mastering 2000+ Days of Nutritious, Healthy Recipes for Weight Loss with Seamless Strategies and a Tailored 30-Day Meal Plan for a Healthy lifestyle.

By Theresa Parker

Table Of Contents

CHAPTER 5: MAIN COURSES 51

CHAPTER 6: DELECTABLE DESSERTS 63

Introduction: Immersion into the Mediterranean Diet

Origins and History of the Mediterranean: Tracing the Culinary Roots

The Mediterranean, a vast expanse of water bordered by three continents, has cradled some of the world's oldest civilizations. It's no surprise, then, that its shores bear the legacy of culinary wonders, each unique, yet intrinsically intertwined. As we embark on this exploration, it's important to first understand how time and diverse cultures have woven the intricate tapestry of the Mediterranean diet.

The Cradle of Civilization

The Mediterranean region has long been the crossroads of the world. From the Phoenicians to the Greeks, from the Romans to the Moors, waves of civilizations have washed over its shores, each leaving a culinary footprint. These ancient cultures, some of the first to establish complex societies, were also among the earliest to recognize the value of the land and sea that surrounded them.

Ancient Greeks, for instance, were not just philosophers and warriors. They were also gourmets who savored the bounty of their lands: olives, wine, and grains. Their feasts, rich in olives and fish, echo in today's Mediterranean meals, emphasizing the value of fresh ingredients and simple preparations.

The Roman Influence

With the expanse of the Roman Empire came the spread of Mediterranean flavors. The Romans introduced viniculture and olives to regions beyond their homeland, such as France and Spain. They were also prolific traders, and their reach brought in ingredients like spices from the East, which were infused into local dishes. It's interesting to ponder that the very act of seasoning our food today carries with it the legacy of ancient trade routes and imperial conquests.

The Middle Ages and the Spice Trade

As time marched on, the Middle Ages brought about a significant culinary revolution in the form of the spice trade. While spices like pepper, cinnamon, and nutmeg had been trickling into the Mediterranean for centuries, the Middle Ages saw an explosive growth in their popularity. Cities like Venice became wealthy hubs, linking the East and West through spice routes. As a result, Mediterranean cuisine started seeing a richer blend of flavors and ingredients, many of which have now become staples.

The Moorish Influence on the Mediterranean Plate

Perhaps one of the most defining culinary influences in the Mediterranean region was the Moors' migration from North Africa. As they settled, particularly in Spain, they introduced a variety of agricultural practices and ingredients, like rice, saffron, citrus fruits, and almonds. These introductions transformed local diets, giving birth to iconic dishes such as the Spanish paella, which marries rice with local meats and seafood, seasoned with precious saffron.

The Renaissance: A Culinary Revival

The Renaissance was not just a rebirth of art and science; it was also a time of gastronomic exploration. This period saw a resurgence in the appreciation of local produce and traditional cooking methods. It emphasized the importance of seasonality, purity, and authenticity in dishes—a philosophy that underpins the Mediterranean diet to this day.

From Tradition to Global Phenomenon

In recent centuries, with the advent of globalization, the Mediterranean diet has expanded its influence far beyond its shores. Immigrants from Mediterranean countries introduced their traditional dishes to new lands, while travelers returning from the region brought with them tales of exotic flavors and vibrant dishes. The world started to recognize not just the deliciousness of Mediterranean cuisine, but also its inherent health benefits.

As science advanced, studies began to link the Mediterranean diet with a range of health benefits, from cardiovascular health to mental well-being. This wasn't just about the ingredients used but also the Mediterranean way of life—where meals are communal affairs, savored without rush, and complemented by the sun's warmth and the sea's freshness.

The Pillars and Benefits of the Mediterranean Diet: Health and Culinary Advantages

When one imagines the Mediterranean, visions of olive groves, sun-ripened tomatoes, lush vineyards, and azure waters teeming with fresh fish often come to mind. These aren't just beautiful postcard images; they represent the fundamental ingredients of the Mediterranean diet.

- **Olives and Olive Oil:** Often referred to as "liquid gold," olive oil is the cornerstone of Mediterranean cuisine. Cold-pressed and unrefined, extra virgin olive oil retains its antioxidants and anti-inflammatory properties, making it both a flavorful and healthful choice for cooking and drizzling.

- **Fresh Vegetables and Fruits:** Seasonality is central to the Mediterranean philosophy. Vegetables and fruits, consumed at the peak of their ripeness, offer maximum flavor and nutritional benefits. Think of the sweetness of a freshly plucked fig or the juiciness of a sun-kissed tomato—these are nature's gifts, abundant in vitamins, minerals, and antioxidants.

- **Fish and Seafood:** With the vast Mediterranean Sea as its heart, it's no surprise that fish and seafood play a pivotal role in the diet. Rich in omega-3 fatty acids, fish like sardines, mackerel, and salmon contribute to heart health and cognitive function.

The Culinary Dance: Techniques and Traditions

Mediterranean cooking isn't just about ingredients; it's also about the reverence with which they're treated. Gentle simmering, grilling over open flames, and the delicate art of sautéing are some of the methods that preserve and enhance the natural flavors and nutrients of the ingredients.

Moreover, spices and herbs like rosemary, basil, oregano, and saffron not only elevate the taste but also introduce additional health benefits. Instead of relying heavily on salts or fats, the Mediterranean approach leans into these natural flavor enhancers, making every dish a harmonious blend of taste and health.

Beyond Nutrition: A Lifestyle of Wholeness

The Mediterranean diet's advantages aren't limited to the plate. This diet encapsulates a holistic approach to life. Meals aren't rushed affairs but are long, leisurely events often shared with family and friends. This fosters a sense of community and well-being, reducing stress and encouraging mindful eating.

Additionally, the Mediterranean lifestyle emphasizes physical activity. Whether it's a gentle stroll through olive orchards or a vigorous dance during a village festa, movement is integral to daily life.

Health Benefits: A Testament to Longevity and Vitality

Numerous studies have lauded the health benefits of the Mediterranean diet. From reduced risks of cardiovascular diseases, certain cancers, and type 2 diabetes to improved brain health and longevity, the advantages are manifold. But beyond statistics and studies, the true testament lies in the vibrant lives of the Mediterranean people, many of whom enjoy good health well into their old age.

The Culinary Delight: A Feast for the Senses

While health is a significant draw, one cannot overlook the sheer culinary pleasure the Mediterranean diet offers. Every meal is a celebration, an explosion of flavors, a sensory journey that tantalizes the taste buds, and warms the soul.

Mediterranean Diet in Daily Life: Strategies and Advice for Easy Integration

At the intersection of tradition and modern living, many wonder how to seamlessly integrate the Mediterranean diet into the hustle and bustle of contemporary life. The secret, however, doesn't lie in grand transformations but in small, mindful adjustments.

Sourcing Fresh and Local

One of the hallmarks of the Mediterranean lifestyle is the emphasis on fresh, local produce. Begin by exploring your local farmers' markets or organic produce stores. Not only do these markets offer fruits and vegetables that are often fresher and more nutrient-rich than supermarket counterparts, but they also encourage a deeper connection to the food you eat. Knowing who grows your food and where it comes from instills a sense of respect and gratitude, enhancing the overall culinary experience.

Rekindling the Joy of Home Cooking

While the modern world is filled with the allure of quick bites and takeaways, the Mediterranean diet underscores the joy and benefits of home cooking. Start simple. Dedicate one or two days of the week to try out Mediterranean recipes. From a hearty Greek salad, fragrant with oregano and feta, to a simple Spanish gazpacho on a hot day, discover the vast array of dishes that are easy to prepare and delightful to the palate.

Savoring Meals: A Time for Bonding and Reflection

In the Mediterranean region, meals aren't just about consumption; they're rituals of bonding, storytelling, and reflection. Try to recreate this ambiance at home. Even if it's just one meal a week, make it a point to gather with family or friends, switch off electronic devices, and engage in genuine conversations. This not only fosters connection but also encourages mindful eating, where you savor each bite, appreciate the flavors, and often, eat just the right amount.

Incorporating Seafood and Plant-Based Proteins

While meats do find a place in the Mediterranean diet, the emphasis is more on seafood and plant-based proteins. Consider diversifying your protein sources. Introduce dishes with lentils, chickpeas, or beans. Plan a "seafood night" where you explore recipes with fish, shrimp, or mussels. These shifts not only align with the Mediterranean philosophy but also offer varied health benefits.

Staying Active: The Mediterranean Way

The Mediterranean lifestyle goes beyond food; it's also about staying active. This doesn't necessarily mean hitting the gym every day but finding joy in everyday activities. It could be a walk in the park, gardening, dancing to your favorite tunes, or even playing a sport. The key is to stay active and make movement a natural part of your routine.

Moderation: The Golden Rule

Whether it's about olive oil, wine, or desserts, the Mediterranean diet teaches the art of moderation. Enjoying a glass of wine is as much a part of the diet as is savoring a piece of baklava. However, the emphasis is always on moderation. Relish these pleasures, but know where to draw the line.

Chapter 1: Essential Guide to Mediterranean Cooking

In the world of gastronomy, the Mediterranean stands as a testament to the marriage of simplicity and flavor. Its cuisine doesn't rely on elaborate techniques, but rather on the purity and essence of each ingredient. However, as simple as it may sound, the foundation of Mediterranean cooking is built on understanding some basic techniques. These techniques, which have been passed down through generations, are pivotal in extracting the richest flavors from the simplest of ingredients.

Basic Techniques: Sautéing, Grilling, Simmering, and More

The word "sauté" hails from the French word for "jump," aptly describing the tossing of ingredients in a pan. This fast cooking method uses a small amount of oil or fat in a shallow pan over relatively high heat. Ingredients are typically cut into small pieces or thinly sliced to facilitate quick cooking.

The beauty of sautéing lies in its ability to seal in the flavors of the main ingredient while allowing complementary ingredients, like herbs and spices, to meld seamlessly. Think of golden-brown garlic slices infused in olive oil, ready to embrace a handful of fresh shrimp or vibrant bell peppers. This technique retains the texture and essence of ingredients, making it a favorite in Mediterranean kitchens.

The Rustic Charm of Grilling

Grilling is not just a technique; it's a social event, a celebration. Across the Mediterranean coast, you'll often find families gathering around a grill, sharing stories, laughter, and the mouthwatering aroma of grilled dishes.

Grilling imparts a smoky flavor to ingredients and, when done correctly, can bring out unparalleled tastes in even the simplest foods. The charred lines on a piece of aubergine, the smoky essence of grilled sardines, or the juicy tenderness of a lamb chop, all bear testimony to the transformative power of the grill in Mediterranean cooking.

The Gentle Embrace of Simmering

Simmering is akin to a gentle lullaby for ingredients, letting them slow-dance in a liquid just below boiling point. It's a technique where patience is rewarded with deep, melded flavors. This method is commonly used for soups, stews, and sauces in Mediterranean cooking.

Envision a pot of tomato sauce, where the tomatoes are left to simmer, breaking down slowly, releasing their juices, and combining with herbs like basil and oregano. Or picture a Moroccan tagine, where lamb is allowed to simmer till it's fork-tender, absorbing the rich flavors of saffron, dates, and almonds.

Discovering More Techniques

Beyond these three foundational methods, Mediterranean cooking embraces a plethora of techniques such as roasting, braising, and marinating. Each method adds a unique touch, a distinct texture, or a specific flavor profile, enriching the culinary tapestry of the region.

Kitchen Must-Haves: Essential Tools and Utensils for Mediterranean Dishes

At the heart of Mediterranean cooking lies its golden nectar - olive oil. And just like wine, its delivery method matters. An olive oil cruet, with its slender spout, ensures a steady, controlled stream, allowing for precision while dressing salads or drizzling over dishes. It also acts as a protector, shielding the oil from excessive exposure to air and light, which can degrade its quality.

The Versatile Mortar and Pestle

This ancient tool, with its humble appearance, is a powerhouse in Mediterranean kitchens. Whether you're crushing fresh garlic with sea salt, grinding saffron for a paella, or making a fragrant pesto, the mortar and pestle extract flavors in ways modern appliances often can't. It brings out the oils and juices from herbs and spices, creating pastes and mixtures full of depth.

A Trustworthy Cast Iron Skillet

Beyond its universal appeal, a cast iron skillet is especially significant for dishes that require both stovetop and oven. Its ability to retain and distribute heat makes it ideal for sautéing vegetables, searing fish, or even baking a traditional Spanish tortilla. With proper care, these skillets can last generations, making them an investment in not just your kitchen but also in the culinary stories you'll pass down.

The Tagine: Morocco's Culinary Gem

Shaped somewhat like a wizard's hat, the tagine is both a cooking vessel and the name of the dishes cooked within it. Its conical lid allows for steam to rise, condense, and drip back down, ensuring the food remains moist. This continuous basting process makes it perfect for slow-cooking meats until they're tender and flavorful, infused with herbs and spices.

A Reliable Chef's Knife

Every kitchen needs a dependable knife. In the realm of Mediterranean cooking, where fresh vegetables, meats, and fish are staples, a sharp, balanced chef's knife can make preparation not only easier but also enjoyable. From finely chopping herbs to deboning a fresh catch, a good knife is indispensable.

Wooden Cooking Utensils

Wooden spoons, spatulas, and ladles have a rustic charm, but their significance goes beyond aesthetics. Wood is gentle on cookware, preventing scratches. It also doesn't conduct heat, ensuring handles remain cool. When stirring a simmering pot of ratatouille or a bubbling sauce, these utensils become an extension of the cook's hand.

Troubleshooting: Resolving Common Cooking Challenges and FAQs

Olive oil, as cherished as it is in this cuisine, can be a tricky companion. A frequent challenge is knowing when it's hot enough to sauté without it reaching its smoke point and becoming bitter. A useful trick is to add a tiny piece of onion or garlic; when it sizzles upon contact, your oil is ready.

The Art of Cooking Seafood Just Right

Seafood is a cornerstone of the Mediterranean diet. However, it's easy to overcook, turning a succulent piece of fish into a dry disappointment. As a rule of thumb, fish is done when it can be easily flaked with a fork. For shrimp, when it turns pink and opaque, it's ready to be savored.

The Mystery of Soggy Vegetables

Mediterranean dishes often celebrate the vibrant crunch of fresh vegetables. If your veggies are coming out limp and overcooked, consider the size you're cutting them into and adjust your cooking time. Another tip is to immerse vegetables in ice water immediately after blanching to retain their crispness.

Rice Challenges: From Paella to Pilaf

Whether it's the Spanish paella or the Greek pilaf, rice dishes can sometimes be unpredictable. If it's undercooked, adding a splash of broth and continuing to cook on low heat can save the day. Overcooked? Transform it into a creamy risotto or a rice pudding, turning a potential mishap into a delightful new dish.

When Your Dish Lacks Depth

Sometimes, despite following a recipe to the letter, the dish might lack the depth or punch you were hoping for. This is where the magic of seasoning comes in. A squeeze of lemon, a dash of a potent herb, or a sprinkle of sea salt can instantly elevate the flavors.

Achieving the Perfect Crust on Breads

Nothing beats the aroma of freshly baked bread wafting through your home. If you're struggling with getting that perfect crust, remember to preheat your oven thoroughly and consider using a baking stone. A pan of hot water placed in the oven can also provide the necessary steam for a crunchy crust.

Making the Most of Leftover Ingredients

There's always that half onion or those few sprigs of herbs left. Instead of letting them go to waste, consider making a flavorful broth or infusing olive oil. Your culinary creativity is the only limit.

Chapter 2: Exploring the Flavors of the Mediterranean

Spanish Cuisine: Dive into Tapas Culture and Iconic Dishes

Nestled on the Iberian Peninsula, Spain boasts a diverse topography, which, over centuries, has led to the evolution of an equally diverse culinary landscape. From the seafood-laden dishes of the coastal regions to the hearty, meat-centric meals of the interiors, Spanish cuisine is a jubilant celebration of its rich history, cultural influences, and abundant local produce.

The Spirit of Tapas

To truly understand Spanish cuisine, one must first immerse oneself in the culture of tapas. More than just a culinary tradition, tapas represents a way of life. It's a social ritual, an invitation to pause, savor, and connect.

Originating from Andalusia in southern Spain, the tradition of tapas began as a simple act: placing a slice of bread or meat (usually ham) over a glass of wine or sherry to keep the flies out. This 'tapa' (meaning 'cover' or 'lid') soon evolved, with innkeepers starting to top these lids with an assortment of nibbles as a way to entice customers.

Today, tapas range from simple olives and almonds to intricate culinary creations, each telling a story of its region, its history, and its people. Walking into a tapas bar in Spain is akin to stepping into a culinary theatre where flavors, aromas, and textures take center stage.

Iconic Dishes that Define Spanish Gastronomy

Paella Valenciana: Hailing from the eastern shores of Spain, paella is more than just a dish; it's an emotion. Cooked in a wide, shallow pan (also called paella), this rice dish, infused with saffron's golden hue, showcases a medley of proteins – from rabbit to chicken, and often seafood. Each region, however, boasts its unique version, honoring its local produce.

Gazpacho: A refreshing antidote to Spain's scorching summers, gazpacho is a cold tomato soup that sings with the freshness of cucumbers, bell peppers, and onions. Originating from Andalusia, it's a testament to the ingenious ways the Spanish have found to stay cool, nourished, and delighted.

Churros con Chocolate: A beloved breakfast treat and dessert, churros are golden, crispy sticks of dough, deep-fried to perfection and sprinkled with sugar. Dunked in a rich, velvety chocolate sauce, it's a pairing that evokes nostalgia and warmth.

Tortilla Española: A humble yet versatile dish, the Spanish omelette is a thick, hearty wedge made from potatoes, eggs, and onions. Enjoyed hot or cold, it's a testament to the magic that arises from the confluence of simple ingredients.

Greece's Gastronomic Wonders: From Moussaka to Olive Oil's Significance

Greece's culinary art is steeped in simplicity. Each dish, though made from straightforward ingredients, holds complex layers of flavors, all beautifully melding together to create a symphony for the taste buds. It's this simplicity that magnifies the natural flavors and wholesomeness of every ingredient used.

Moussaka: The Layered Delight

If there's one dish that resonates with the essence of Greek cuisine, it's the sumptuous moussaka. Picture layers of thinly sliced aubergines, succulent minced meat simmered in a tomato-based sauce, and velvety béchamel—all baked to perfection. Each bite of moussaka feels like a warm hug, reminding you of the love and care infused in Greek cooking.

The Elixir of Greece: Olive Oil

Olive oil in Greek cuisine is not just a cooking medium; it's the lifeblood that courses through every dish. From salads drizzled generously with it to breads dipped into its golden richness, olive oil is the unsung hero that uplifts every meal. Greece, home to some of the world's oldest olive trees, cherishes its liquid gold. The process of cultivating olives and extracting their oil is an art passed down generations. The significance of olive oil doesn't stop at the kitchen door; it extends to rituals, religious ceremonies, and traditional medicines. It's a symbol of peace, wisdom, and victory.

Tzatziki: The Cool Companion

No Greek meal is complete without a serving of tzatziki, a refreshing yogurt-based dip laced with cucumbers, garlic, and dill. It's the perfect accompaniment to grilled meats, a dip for pita bread, or even a delightful spread on sandwiches. Its cooling properties make it a staple during the hot Grecian summers.

The Aegean on a Plate

Greece, with its extensive coastline and myriad islands, offers a treasure trove of seafood dishes. From the simple grilled octopus seasoned with just a hint of lemon and oregano to the rich, tomato-based fish stews, the bounty of the Aegean Sea graces Greek tables in all its splendor.

From Ancient Times to Contemporary Tables

Greek cuisine, like its magnificent ruins and age-old tales, stands as a testament to the country's rich history. From the times of Homer's Iliad and Odyssey, where feasts and foods were often described, to today's bustling tavernas, the spirit of Greek food remains unchanged.

The mingling of various civilizations on this land, from the Ottomans to the Venetians, has also left indelible imprints on its culinary landscape. Yet, amidst these influences, Greek food has retained its identity, exuding warmth, generosity, and a deep connection to the land and sea.

Italian Delights: The Diverse World of Pasta, Risotto, and Cheeses

When one thinks of Italy, visions of rolling vineyards, historical landmarks, passionate opera, and most importantly, its unmatched culinary prowess come to mind. The country, shaped like a boot and nestled in the heart of the Mediterranean, boasts a food culture that is diverse, regional, and deeply rooted in centuries-old traditions.

A Love Affair with Pasta

In the vast world of Italian cuisine, pasta reigns supreme. From the cobblestoned streets of Rome to the waterways of Venice, pasta dishes vary in shape, size, and flavor, each telling the story of its origin. In Bologna, you might find yourself indulging in the rich and meaty "Ragu alla Bolognese", while in Naples, the simplicity of "Spaghetti aglio e olio" - spaghetti with garlic, oil, and a sprinkle of chili - showcases the elegance of minimalism.

However, pasta is not just about the sauce it's cloaked in; the shape and texture play a pivotal role in the dining experience. There's a reason why certain sauces are paired with specific pasta shapes. The ridges in penne, for instance, hold onto meaty sauces, while the hollows in conchiglie (shells) capture bits of vegetables or cheese.

Risotto: The Symphony of Rice and Broth

If pasta rules the realm of Italian main courses, risotto is its regal counterpart. Originating from Northern Italy, where rice paddies are abundant, risotto is a creamy rice dish cooked slowly with broth. The magic lies in the constant stirring, which releases the rice's natural starches, giving risotto its signature creamy texture.

While the base remains consistent, the flavors of risotto can range from the earthiness of mushrooms in "Risotto ai Funghi" to the luxury of saffron in the Milanese classic "Risotto alla Milanese."

Cheese: The Heartbeat of Italian Gastronomy

Italy's love for cheese is profound. From the sharp and hard Grana Padano to the soft and creamy burrata, each region boasts its cheese, integral to both cooking and direct consumption. Take, for example, the mozzarella from Campania, a cheese so revered it's often enjoyed on its own, drizzled with a little olive oil, or the pungent gorgonzola with its blue veins, adding depth to pasta sauces and salads alike.

Parmesan, or "Parmigiano Reggiano", deserves special mention. Aged for years, this cheese is a staple in Italian kitchens, often grated over dishes or eaten in chunks, accompanied by a drizzle of aged balsamic vinegar.

From Vineyards to Seaside Taverns

No journey through Italian cuisine is complete without acknowledging the role of its wines and seafood. Regions like Tuscany and Piedmont are world-renowned for their wines, enhancing the dining experience and often playing a role in cooking as well. Along the coastline, dishes showcase the Mediterranean's bounty, with calamari, shrimp, and various fish taking center stage, often simply grilled and flavored with herbs and olive oil.

Chapter 3: Starters, Snacks, and Light Bites

FRESH TOMATO BRUSCHETTA

P.T.: 10 mins

C.T.: 5 mins

INGR:

- 1 baguette, sliced into 1/2-inch thick rounds
- 3 ripe tomatoes, diced
- 2 garlic cloves, minced
- 3 tbsp olive oil
- salt and pepper to taste

PROCEDURE:

1. Preheat oven to 375°F (190°C).
2. Drizzle slices of baguette with 1 tbsp of olive oil and toast in the oven until golden brown.
3. In a bowl, mix tomatoes, garlic, remaining olive oil, salt, and pepper.
4. Spoon the tomato mixture onto the toasted baguette slices.
5. Serve immediately.

TIPS: Use heirloom tomatoes for an extra flavor kick.

N.V.: Calories: 80, Carbs: 10g, Protein: 2g, Fat: 4g

SIMPLE FETA CHEESE DIP

P.T.: 10 mins

C.T.: 0 mins

INGR:

- 1 cup feta cheese, crumbled
- A quarter cup olive oil
- 1 tbsp lemon zest
- 1 tbsp freshly squeezed lemon juice
- 1/2 tsp crushed red pepper flakes

PROCEDURE:

1. In a mixing bowl, combine feta cheese and olive oil.
2. Add lemon zest and lemon juice.
3. Sprinkle in crushed red pepper flakes.
4. Mix well until smooth.
5. Transfer to a serving bowl.

TIPS: Serve with fresh pita bread or sliced cucumbers.

N.V.: Calories: 90, Carbs: 1g, Protein: 3g, Fat: 8g

ZUCCHINI AND MINT FRITTERS

P.T.: 15 mins

C.T.: 10 mins

INGR:

- 2 zucchinis, grated
- 1/2 cup fresh mint leaves, chopped
- 1 egg
- 2 tbsp olive oil
- salt and pepper to taste

PROCEDURE:

1. In a bowl, combine grated zucchini, mint, egg, salt, and pepper.
2. Heat olive oil in a pan over medium heat.
3. Scoop out tablespoonfuls of the zucchini mixture and drop into the pan, flattening slightly.
4. Cook for 4-5 minutes on each side or until golden.
5. Place on paper towels to drain excess oil.

TIPS: Serve with a side of tzatziki or plain yogurt.

N.V.: Calories: 70, Carbs: 3g, Protein: 2g, Fat: 6g

OLIVE TAPENADE CROSTINI

P.T.: 10 mins

C.T.: 5 mins

INGR:

- 1 cup pitted mixed olives
- 2 garlic cloves
- 2 tbsp capers
- 3 tbsp olive oil
- 1 baguette, sliced

PROCEDURE:

1. In a food processor, combine olives, garlic, capers, and olive oil until coarsely chopped.
2. Toast baguette slices in oven at 375°F (190°C) for 5 minutes.
3. Spread olive tapenade on toasted baguette slices.
4. Drizzle with additional olive oil if desired.
5. Serve immediately.

TIPS: Store leftover tapenade in an airtight container in the fridge.

N.V.: Calories: 80, Carbs: 11g, Protein: 2g, Fat: 4g

QUICK MARINATED ARTICHOKES

P.T.: 10 mins

C.T.: 0 mins

INGR:

- 1 cup canned artichoke hearts, drained
- A quarter cup olive oil
- 1 tbsp lemon juice
- 1 garlic clove, minced
- salt and pepper to taste

PROCEDURE:

1. In a bowl, whisk together olive oil, lemon juice, garlic, salt, and pepper.
2. Add artichoke hearts to the bowl and toss to coat.
3. Allow to marinate for at least 30 minutes before serving.
4. Transfer to a serving dish.
5. Drizzle with additional olive oil if desired.

TIPS: Pair with a glass of crisp white wine.

N.V.: Calories: 70, Carbs: 4g, Protein: 1g, Fat: 6g

MEDITERRANEAN STUFFED PEPPERS

P.T.: 20 mins

C.T.: 25 mins

INGR:

- 2 large bell peppers, halved and seeds removed
- 1 cup cooked quinoa
- 1/2 cup cherry tomatoes, halved
- A quarter cup crumbled feta cheese
- 2 tbsp olive oil

PROCEDURE:

1. Preheat oven to 375°F (190°C).
2. In a bowl, combine quinoa, cherry tomatoes, feta, and olive oil.
3. Stuff each pepper half with the quinoa mixture.
4. Place in a baking dish and cover with foil.
5. Bake for 25 minutes or until the peppers are tender.

TIPS: Garnish with fresh parsley or basil before serving.

N.V.: Calories: 110, Carbs: 12g, Protein: 4g, Fat: 6g

SPICY LEMON HUMMUS

P.T.: 10 mins

C.T.: 0 mins

INGR:

- 1 can (15 oz) chickpeas, drained and rinsed
- 2 tbsp tahini
- 2 garlic cloves
- 1 tbsp olive oil
- juice of 1 lemon

PROCEDURE:

1. In a food processor, combine chickpeas, tahini, garlic, olive oil, and lemon juice.
2. Blend until smooth and creamy.
3. Transfer to a bowl and drizzle with more olive oil if desired.
4. Serve with sliced cucumbers or pita chips.

TIPS: Add a pinch of cayenne pepper for extra heat.

N.V.: Calories: 100, Carbs: 12g, Protein: 4g, Fat: 5g

EASY MEDITERRANEAN CUCUMBER SALAD

P.T.: 15 mins

C.T.: 0 mins

INGR:

- 2 cucumbers, thinly sliced
- 1/2 red onion, thinly sliced
- A quarter cup Kalamata olives, pitted
- 2 tbsp olive oil
- 1 tbsp red wine vinegar

PROCEDURE:

1. In a bowl, combine cucumbers, red onion, and olives.
2. Drizzle with olive oil and red wine vinegar.
3. Toss to combine and refrigerate for at least 30 minutes before serving.

TIPS: Top with crumbled feta cheese for extra flavor.

N.V.: Calories: 60, Carbs: 5g, Protein: 1g, Fat: 4g

GREEK YOGURT TZATZIKI DIP

P.T.: 10 mins

C.T.: 0 mins

INGR:

- 1 cup Greek yogurt
- 1 cucumber, finely diced
- 2 garlic cloves, minced
- 1 tbsp dill, chopped
- juice of 1/2 lemon

PROCEDURE:

1. In a bowl, mix Greek yogurt, cucumber, garlic, dill, and lemon juice.
2. Chill in the refrigerator for at least 1 hour before serving.
3. Serve with fresh vegetables or pita bread.

TIPS: For a creamier texture, use full-fat Greek yogurt.

N.V.: Calories: 50, Carbs: 4g, Protein: 6g, Fat: 1g

BAKED FALAFEL BITES

P.T.: 20 mins

C.T.: 25 mins

INGR:

- 1 can (15 oz) chickpeas, drained and rinsed
- A quarter cup fresh parsley, chopped
- 2 garlic cloves
- 1 tsp cumin
- 1 tbsp olive oil

PROCEDURE:

1. Preheat oven to 375°F (190°C).
2. In a food processor, combine chickpeas, parsley, garlic, cumin, and olive oil.
3. Pulse until a coarse mixture forms.
4. Shape into small balls and place on a baking sheet.
5. Bake for 25 minutes or until golden brown.

TIPS: Serve with tzatziki dip or in a pita pocket with fresh vegetables.

N.V.: Calories: 90, Carbs: 12g, Protein: 4g, Fat: 3g

CHERRY TOMATO AND BASIL SKEWERS

P.T.: 10 mins

C.T.: 0 mins

INGR:

- 1 cup cherry tomatoes
- 1/2 cup fresh basil leaves
- 125g mozzarella balls
- 2 tbsp balsamic glaze
- 1 tbsp olive oil

PROCEDURE:

1. Thread a cherry tomato, a basil leaf, and a mozzarella ball onto a skewer.
2. Repeat until all ingredients are used.
3. Drizzle with olive oil and balsamic glaze.
4. Serve immediately.

TIPS: For a savory twist, sprinkle with a little sea salt before serving.

N.V.: Calories: 70, Carbs: 5g, Protein: 3g, Fat: 4g

SPINACH AND FETA STUFFED MUSHROOMS

P.T.: 15 mins

C.T.: 20 mins

INGR:

- 12 large button mushrooms, stems removed
- 1 cup fresh spinach, chopped
- 1/2 cup crumbled feta cheese
- 2 garlic cloves, minced
- 1 tbsp olive oil

PROCEDURE:

1. Preheat oven to 375°F (190°C).
2. In a pan, heat olive oil and sauté garlic for a minute.
3. Add spinach and cook until wilted.
4. Remove from heat and stir in crumbled feta.
5. Stuff each mushroom cap with the spinach and feta mixture.
6. Place on a baking tray and bake for 20 minutes or until mushrooms are tender.

TIPS: Garnish with chopped parsley or drizzle with lemon juice before serving.

N.V.: Calories: 50, Carbs: 3g, Protein: 2g, Fat: 3g

LEMON AND ROSEMARY OLIVES

P.T.: 10 mins

C.T.: 0 mins

INGR:

- 2 cups mixed olives
- 1 lemon, zest and juice
- 2 sprigs fresh rosemary, chopped
- 3 tbsp olive oil
- 1/2 tsp crushed red pepper flakes (optional)

PROCEDURE:

1. In a bowl, combine olives, lemon zest, lemon juice, and rosemary.
2. Drizzle with olive oil and sprinkle with red pepper flakes if desired.
3. Toss well to coat.
4. Let marinate for at least 30 minutes before serving.

TIPS: These marinated olives can be stored in an airtight container in the refrigerator for up to a week.

N.V.: Calories: 100, Carbs: 3g, Protein: 0g, Fat: 10g

AUBERGINE AND YOGURT SPREAD

P.T.: 10 mins

C.T.: 25 mins

INGR:

- 1 large aubergine (eggplant)
- 1/2 cup Greek yogurt
- 2 garlic cloves, minced
- 1 tbsp olive oil
- 1 tbsp lemon juice

PROCEDURE:

1. Preheat oven to 400°F (200°C).
2. Prick the aubergine with a fork and place on a baking sheet.
3. Bake for 25 minutes or until tender.
4. Once cooled, peel and chop the aubergine.
5. In a bowl, mix aubergine, Greek yogurt, garlic, olive oil, and lemon juice.

TIPS: Serve chilled with pita chips or fresh vegetables.

N.V.: Calories: 80, Carbs: 10g, Protein: 3g, Fat: 4g

MEDITERRANEAN SHRIMP COCKTAIL

P.T.: 10 mins

C.T.: 5 mins

INGR:

- 1 lb large shrimp, peeled and deveined
- 2 tbsp olive oil
- 1 lemon, zest and juice
- A quarter cup fresh parsley, chopped
- 1 garlic clove, minced

PROCEDURE:

1. In a pan, heat olive oil and sauté garlic for a minute.
2. Add shrimp and cook for 2-3 minutes on each side or until pink and opaque.
3. Remove from heat and place in a bowl.
4. Toss with lemon zest, lemon juice, and chopped parsley.
5. Chill before serving.

TIPS: Serve with a tangy cocktail sauce or tzatziki dip.

N.V.: Calories: 90, Carbs: 1g, Protein: 18g, Fat: 2g

Chapter 4: Hearty Soups And Stews

TOMATO AND LENTIL SOUP

P.T.: 10 mins

C.T.: 25 mins

INGR:

- 1 cup red lentils
- 3 cups diced tomatoes (canned or fresh)
- 1 onion, chopped
- 2 garlic cloves, minced
- 4 cups vegetable broth

PROCEDURE:

1. In a large pot, sauté onions and garlic until translucent.
2. Add lentils, tomatoes, and vegetable broth.
3. Bring to a boil, then reduce to simmer.
4. Cook for 20-25 minutes or until lentils are tender.
5. Blend with an immersion blender for a creamy texture or leave as is.

TIPS: Garnish with fresh basil or croutons before serving.

N.V.: Calories: 150, Carbs: 28g, Protein: 9g, Fat: 1g

SPINACH AND WHITE BEAN STEW

P.T.: 15 mins

C.T.: 30 mins

INGR:

- 2 cups fresh spinach, roughly chopped
- 1 can white beans, drained and rinsed
- 1 onion, chopped
- 2 garlic cloves, minced
- 4 cups chicken or vegetable broth

PROCEDURE:

1. In a pot, sauté onion and garlic until golden.
2. Add white beans and broth, bring to a simmer.
3. Cook for 20 minutes.
4. Add chopped spinach, stir until wilted.

5. Serve hot.

TIPS: Drizzle with a dash of olive oil or sprinkle with feta cheese.

N.V.: Calories: 130, Carbs: 22g, Protein: 8g, Fat: 2g

ROASTED PEPPER AND ZUCCHINI SOUP

P.T.: 15 mins

C.T.: 25 mins

INGR:

- 2 red bell peppers, roasted and peeled
- 2 zucchinis, diced
- 1 onion, chopped
- 1 garlic clove, minced
- 3 cups vegetable broth

PROCEDURE:

1. In a pot, sauté onion and garlic until soft.
2. Add diced zucchinis, roasted peppers, and broth.
3. Bring to a boil, then reduce to simmer.
4. Cook until zucchinis are tender.
5. Blend to desired consistency.

TIPS: Serve with a dollop of Greek yogurt or fresh mint leaves.

N.V.: Calories: 80, Carbs: 17g, Protein: 3g, Fat: 0.5g

LEMON AND ORZO CHICKEN SOUP

P.T.: 10 mins

C.T.: 30 mins

INGR:

- 2 chicken breasts, diced
- 1 cup orzo pasta
- 1 lemon, zest and juice
- 4 cups chicken broth
- 1 carrot, diced

PROCEDURE:

1. In a pot, cook diced chicken until browned.
2. Add carrot and sauté for a few minutes.
3. Pour in chicken broth and bring to a simmer.
4. Add orzo pasta, cook until al dente.
5. Stir in lemon zest and juice.

TIPS: Top with chopped parsley or grated Parmesan cheese.

N.V.: Calories: 190, Carbs: 24g, Protein: 14g, Fat: 4g

MEDITERRANEAN FISH STEW

P.T.: 15 mins

C.T.: 20 mins

INGR:

- 2 fillets of white fish (like cod or tilapia), diced
- 1 can diced tomatoes
- 1 onion, chopped
- 2 garlic cloves, minced
- 3 cups fish or vegetable broth

PROCEDURE:

1. Sauté onion and garlic in a pot until translucent.
2. Add diced tomatoes and broth.
3. Bring to a simmer, then add diced fish.
4. Cook until fish is opaque and easily flakes with a fork.
5. Season with salt, pepper, and herbs of choice.

TIPS: Garnish with fresh dill or serve with a slice of crusty bread.

N.V.: Calories: 140, Carbs: 9g, Protein: 17g, Fat: 3g

ARTICHOKE AND POTATO SOUP

P.T.: 15 mins

C.T.: 30 mins

INGR:

- 2 large potatoes, diced
- 1 can artichoke hearts, drained and chopped
- 1 onion, diced
- 2 garlic cloves, minced
- 4 cups vegetable broth

PROCEDURE:

1. Sauté onion and garlic in a large pot until translucent.
2. Add diced potatoes, artichoke hearts, and broth.
3. Bring to a boil, then simmer until potatoes are tender.
4. Use an immersion blender to create a smoother texture if desired.
5. Season with salt and pepper to taste.

TIPS: Add a splash of lemon juice or top with fresh parsley.

N.V.: Calories: 130, Carbs: 29g, Protein: 3g, Fat: 0.5g

MUSHROOM AND BARLEY STEW

P.T.: 15 mins

C.T.: 45 mins

INGR:

- 1 cup barley, rinsed
- 2 cups mushrooms, sliced
- 1 onion, chopped
- 2 garlic cloves, minced
- 5 cups beef or vegetable broth

PROCEDURE:

1. In a pot, sauté onions, garlic, and mushrooms until soft.
2. Add barley and broth.
3. Bring to a boil, then reduce to a simmer.
4. Cook until barley is tender, stirring occasionally.
5. Season with salt, pepper, and thyme.

TIPS: A dollop of sour cream or Greek yogurt complements the earthy flavors.

N.V.: Calories: 170, Carbs: 35g, Protein: 6g, Fat: 1g

CHICKPEA AND CHARD SOUP

P.T.: 10 mins

C.T.: 25 mins

INGR:

- 1 can chickpeas, drained and rinsed
- 2 cups chard, chopped
- 1 onion, diced
- 2 garlic cloves, minced
- 4 cups chicken or vegetable broth

PROCEDURE:

1. Sauté onion and garlic in a pot until golden.
2. Add chickpeas and broth, and bring to a simmer.
3. After 15 minutes, add chard until wilted.
4. Season with salt, pepper, and a pinch of paprika.
5. Serve hot.

TIPS: Garnish with a sprinkle of feta or a squeeze of lemon.

N.V.: Calories: 140, Carbs: 24g, Protein: 7g, Fat: 2g

FENNEL AND SAUSAGE STEW

P.T.: 15 mins

C.T.: 30 mins

INGR:

- 2 sausages, sliced
- 1 large fennel bulb, chopped
- 1 onion, chopped
- 2 garlic cloves, minced
- 4 cups chicken broth

PROCEDURE:

1. In a pot, brown sausage slices.
2. Add onion, garlic, and fennel. Sauté until soft.
3. Pour in chicken broth and bring to a simmer.
4. Cook until fennel is tender and flavors meld.
5. Season with salt and black pepper.

TIPS: Finish with fresh dill or a splash of white wine.

N.V.: Calories: 210, Carbs: 14g, Protein: 12g, Fat: 12g

EGGPLANT AND TOMATO STEW

P.T.: 15 mins

C.T.: 35 mins

INGR:

- 1 large eggplant, diced
- 3 cups diced tomatoes (canned or fresh)
- 1 onion, diced
- 2 garlic cloves, minced
- 4 cups vegetable broth

PROCEDURE:

1. Sauté onion and garlic in a large pot until soft.
2. Add diced eggplant and tomatoes.
3. Pour in broth and bring to a boil.
4. Reduce to simmer and cook until eggplant is tender.
5. Season with herbs like basil or oregano, salt, and pepper.

TIPS: Garnish with fresh parsley or serve with toasted pita bread.

N.V.: Calories: 90, Carbs: 20g, Protein: 3g, Fat: 1g

PUMPKIN AND SAGE SOUP

P.T.: 10 mins

C.T.: 25 mins

INGR:

- 2 cups pumpkin puree
- 4 cups vegetable broth
- 1 onion, chopped
- 2 garlic cloves, minced
- 1 tbsp fresh sage, chopped

PROCEDURE:

1. In a pot, sauté onion and garlic until translucent.
2. Add pumpkin puree, sage, and broth.
3. Bring to a simmer, stirring occasionally.
4. Cook for 20-25 minutes, allowing flavors to blend.
5. Adjust seasoning with salt and pepper.

TIPS: Serve with a swirl of cream or crumbled goat cheese.

N.V.: Calories: 70, Carbs: 16g, Protein: 2g, Fat: 0.5g

BEET AND DILL SOUP

P.T.: 15 mins

C.T.: 35 mins

INGR:

- 3 large beets, peeled and diced
- 1 onion, chopped
- 2 garlic cloves, minced
- 4 cups vegetable broth
- 2 tbsp fresh dill, chopped

PROCEDURE:

1. Sauté onion and garlic in a pot until soft.
2. Add diced beets and vegetable broth.
3. Bring to a boil, then simmer until beets are tender.
4. Blend to desired consistency and stir in fresh dill.
5. Season with salt and pepper.

TIPS: Top with a dollop of sour cream or yogurt.

N.V.: Calories: 90, Carbs: 20g, Protein: 3g, Fat: 0.5g

CELERY ROOT AND PEAR SOUP

P.T.: 10 mins

C.T.: 30 mins

INGR:

- 1 large celery root, peeled and diced
- 2 pears, cored and chopped
- 1 onion, chopped
- 2 garlic cloves, minced
- 4 cups vegetable broth

PROCEDURE:

1. In a pot, sauté onion and garlic until golden.
2. Add celery root, pears, and broth.
3. Bring to a boil, then simmer until celery root is soft.
4. Blend until smooth.
5. Season with salt, pepper, and a hint of nutmeg.

TIPS: Garnish with roasted hazelnuts or fresh chives.

N.V.: Calories: 110, Carbs: 25g, Protein: 3g, Fat: 1g

OLIVE AND LEMON CHICKEN STEW

P.T.: 15 mins

C.T.: 40 mins

INGR:

- 2 chicken breasts, diced
- 1 cup green olives, pitted and halved
- 1 lemon, zest and juice
- 1 onion, chopped
- 4 cups chicken broth

PROCEDURE:

1. Brown chicken in a pot, then remove and set aside.
2. Sauté onion until translucent.
3. Return chicken to the pot, add olives, lemon zest, and broth.
4. Simmer for 30-35 minutes.
5. Stir in lemon juice before serving.

TIPS: Serve with crusty bread or a sprinkle of fresh parsley.

N.V.: Calories: 180, Carbs: 8g, Protein: 24g, Fat: 7g

SWEET POTATO AND ROSEMARY SOUP

P.T.: 10 mins

C.T.: 30 mins

INGR:

- 2 large sweet potatoes, peeled and diced
- 1 onion, chopped
- 2 garlic cloves, minced
- 4 cups vegetable broth
- 1 tbsp fresh rosemary, chopped

PROCEDURE:

1. Sauté onion and garlic in a pot until soft.
2. Add sweet potatoes, rosemary, and broth.
3. Bring to a boil, then reduce to simmer.
4. Cook until sweet potatoes are tender.
5. Blend until smooth and season with salt and pepper.

TIPS: Drizzle with olive oil or sprinkle with roasted pumpkin seeds.

N.V.: Calories: 120, Carbs: 28g, Protein: 2g, Fat: 1g

LENTIL AND SPINACH SOUP

P.T.: 10 mins

C.T.: 40 mins

INGR:

- 1 cup green lentils, rinsed
- 3 cups spinach, roughly chopped
- 1 onion, diced
- 2 garlic cloves, minced
- 4 cups vegetable broth

PROCEDURE:

1. Sauté the onion and garlic in a large pot until soft.
2. Add lentils and vegetable broth, bringing to a boil.
3. Reduce heat and simmer until lentils are nearly tender.
4. Stir in spinach and cook until wilted.
5. Season with salt, pepper, and a dash of cumin.

TIPS: Serve with a wedge of lemon on the side for extra zest.

N.V.: Calories: 150, Carbs: 25g, Protein: 10g, Fat: 1g

WHITE BEAN AND ROSEMARY STEW

P.T.: 10 mins

C.T.: 30 mins

INGR:

- 1 can white beans, drained and rinsed
- 1 tomato, diced
- 1 onion, chopped
- 2 garlic cloves, minced
- 4 cups vegetable broth
- 1 tbsp fresh rosemary, chopped

PROCEDURE:

1. In a pot, sauté onion and garlic until translucent.
2. Add beans, tomato, rosemary, and broth.
3. Bring to a boil, then simmer for 25 minutes.
4. Season with salt, pepper, and a drizzle of olive oil.
5. Serve warm.

TIPS: Grate some pecorino cheese on top for an added flavor boost.

N.V.: Calories: 140, Carbs: 23g, Protein: 8g, Fat: 2g

CARROT AND ORANGE SOUP

P.T.: 10 mins

C.T.: 25 mins

INGR:

- 5 large carrots, peeled and chopped
- 1 orange, zest and juice
- 1 onion, diced
- 2 garlic cloves, minced
- 4 cups vegetable broth

PROCEDURE:

1. Sauté the onion and garlic in a pot until soft.
2. Add carrots, broth, orange zest, and juice.
3. Bring to a boil, then simmer until carrots are tender.
4. Blend until smooth.
5. Season with salt and a pinch of nutmeg.

TIPS: Garnish with fresh mint or a dollop of yogurt.

N.V.: Calories: 90, Carbs: 22g, Protein: 2g, Fat: 0.5g

LAMB AND APRICOT STEW

P.T.: 15 mins

C.T.: 45 mins

INGR:

- 2 lamb shanks, bone-in
- 5 dried apricots, chopped
- 1 onion, chopped
- 2 garlic cloves, minced
- 4 cups beef broth

PROCEDURE:

1. Brown the lamb shanks in a large pot, then set aside.
2. In the same pot, sauté onion and garlic.
3. Return lamb to the pot, add apricots and broth.
4. Bring to a boil, then reduce to a simmer, cooking until lamb is tender.
5. Season with salt, pepper, and a sprinkle of cinnamon.

TIPS: Serve over couscous with toasted almonds.

N.V.: Calories: 300, Carbs: 20g, Protein: 28g, Fat: 12g

BROCCOLI AND ALMOND SOUP

P.T.: 10 mins

C.T.: 25 mins

INGR:

- 2 large heads of broccoli, chopped
- A quarter cup almond slivers, toasted
- 1 onion, diced
- 2 garlic cloves, minced
- 4 cups vegetable broth

PROCEDURE:

1. Sauté the onion and garlic in a pot until golden.
2. Add broccoli and vegetable broth.
3. Bring to a boil, then simmer until broccoli is tender.
4. Blend the soup, adding most of the almonds, reserving some for garnish.
5. Season with salt and pepper.

TIPS: Garnish with reserved toasted almonds and a drizzle of olive oil.

N.V.: Calories: 110, Carbs: 15g, Protein: 5g, Fat: 4g

Chapter 5: Main Courses

MEDITERRANEAN CHICKEN THIGHS

P.T.: 15 mins

C.T.: 25 mins

INGR:

- 4 chicken thighs, bone-in and skin-on
- 2 lemons, sliced
- A quarter cup olives, pitted and chopped
- 3 garlic cloves, minced
- 2 tbsp olive oil

PROCEDURE:

1. Preheat oven to 400°F (200°C).
2. Sear the chicken thighs in olive oil until skin is crispy.
3. Scatter the lemon slices, olives, and minced garlic around the chicken.
4. Bake in the oven for 20 minutes or until chicken is cooked through.
5. Serve hot with some of the pan juices drizzled over.

TIPS: Accompany with a fresh Greek salad for a light and balanced meal.

N.V.: Calories: 320, Carbs: 5g, Protein: 22g, Fat: 24g

SPINACH AND FETA STUFFED TOMATOES

P.T.: 15 mins

C.T.: 20 mins

INGR:

- 4 large tomatoes
- 1 cup spinach, chopped
- 1/2 cup feta cheese, crumbled
- 1 garlic clove, minced
- 2 tbsp olive oil

PROCEDURE:

1. Preheat oven to 375°F (190°C).
2. Cut off the tops of the tomatoes and hollow them out.
3. In a bowl, mix spinach, feta, garlic, and olive oil.
4. Stuff each tomato with the spinach mixture.
5. Bake for 20 minutes until tomatoes are tender and the filling is heated through.

TIPS: Drizzle with balsamic reduction for an added layer of flavor.

N.V.: Calories: 150, Carbs: 7g, Protein: 5g, Fat: 12g

SEAFOOD PAELLA

P.T.: 20 mins

C.T.: 40 mins

INGR:

- 1 cup Arborio rice
- 1/2 cup mixed seafood (shrimp, mussels, squid)
- 1 bell pepper, sliced
- 1 onion, chopped
- 3 cups chicken broth
- 1 pinch of saffron

PROCEDURE:

1. Sauté onion and bell pepper in a paella pan with some olive oil.
2. Add the rice and stir to coat with the onion mixture.
3. Pour in chicken broth and saffron, then arrange the seafood on top.
4. Cook on medium heat until the rice is tender and the liquid is absorbed.
5. Serve with lemon wedges on the side.

TIPS: Garnish with fresh parsley and a sprinkle of smoked paprika.

N.V.: Calories: 300, Carbs: 52g, Protein: 14g, Fat: 4g

GRILLED LAMB KOFTAS

P.T.: 20 mins

C.T.: 15 mins

INGR:

- 1 lb lamb mince
- 1 tsp cumin
- 2 tbsp fresh mint, chopped
- 1 onion, finely grated
- 1 garlic clove, minced

PROCEDURE:

1. Combine all ingredients in a bowl and mix thoroughly.
2. Shape the mixture into oval shapes and thread onto skewers.
3. Preheat grill and cook koftas for about 7 minutes on each side.
4. Serve with tzatziki sauce and warm pita bread.
5. Garnish with extra mint.

TIPS: Add a touch of cinnamon to the lamb mixture for a unique twist.

N.V.: Calories: 320, Carbs: 5g, Protein: 20g, Fat: 24g

AUBERGINE (EGGPLANT) PARMIGIANA

P.T.: 15 mins

C.T.: 40 mins

INGR:

- 2 large aubergines (eggplants), sliced
- 1 cup tomato sauce
- 1/2 cup mozzarella, grated
- A quarter cup Parmesan cheese, grated
- 1 garlic clove, minced

PROCEDURE:

1. Grill aubergine slices until slightly charred and tender.
2. In a baking dish, layer aubergine, tomato sauce, mozzarella, garlic, and Parmesan.
3. Repeat layers until all ingredients are used up, finishing with a layer of cheese on top.
4. Bake at 375°F (190°C) for 30 minutes until bubbly and golden.
5. Let it rest for 5 minutes before serving.

TIPS: Serve with a fresh basil and arugula salad.

N.V.: Calories: 190, Carbs: 15g, Protein: 9g, Fat: 11g

HERB-INFUSED SEA BASS

P.T.: 10 mins

C.T.: 20 mins

INGR:

- 2 sea bass fillets
- 1 lemon, zest and juice
- 2 tbsp olive oil
- 1 tsp mixed herbs (thyme, rosemary, parsley)
- 1 garlic clove, minced

PROCEDURE:

1. Mix olive oil, lemon zest, lemon juice, herbs, and garlic in a bowl.
2. Marinade the sea bass fillets in this mixture for 10 minutes.
3. Preheat grill and cook the fillets for about 5 minutes on each side until cooked through.
4. Serve on a bed of sautéed spinach with a wedge of lemon.
5. Drizzle with some of the remaining marinade.

TIPS: For added crispiness, sear the skin side of the fillets on high heat for a minute.

N.V.: Calories: 220, Carbs: 2g, Protein: 23g, Fat: 14g

SPINACH AND RICOTTA CANNELLONI

P.T.: 20 mins

C.T.: 30 mins

INGR:

- 8 cannelloni tubes
- 1 cup ricotta cheese
- 1 cup spinach, cooked and chopped
- 1 garlic clove, minced
- 1 cup tomato sauce

PROCEDURE:

1. Mix ricotta, spinach, and garlic in a bowl.
2. Fill each cannelloni tube with the ricotta mixture.
3. Lay filled tubes in a baking dish and cover with tomato sauce.
4. Bake at 375°F (190°C) for 30 minutes until pasta is cooked and the top is bubbly.
5. Garnish with grated Parmesan cheese and fresh basil.

TIPS: Serve with a green salad and crusty bread for a complete meal.

N.V.: Calories: 280, Carbs: 32g, Protein: 14g, Fat: 10g

ROASTED RED PEPPER HUMMUS BOWL

P.T.: 15 mins

C.T.: 0 mins

INGR:

- 1 cup chickpeas, cooked
- 1 roasted red pepper, chopped
- 1 garlic clove, minced
- 2 tbsp tahini
- 1 lemon, juiced

PROCEDURE:

1. In a blender, combine chickpeas, roasted red pepper, garlic, tahini, and lemon juice.
2. Blend until smooth, adding a bit of water if needed.
3. Transfer to a bowl and make a small well in the center.
4. Drizzle with olive oil and sprinkle with paprika.
5. Garnish with chopped parsley and serve with pita chips.

TIPS: Add a sprinkle of cumin for a deeper flavor.

N.V.: Calories: 190, Carbs: 23g, Protein: 7g, Fat: 9g

GARLIC AND CHILI PRAWN PASTA

P.T.: 10 mins

C.T.: 15 mins

INGR:

- 200g spaghetti
- 1 cup prawns, peeled and deveined
- 2 garlic cloves, minced
- 1 red chili, finely sliced
- 2 tbsp olive oil

PROCEDURE:

1. Cook the spaghetti according to package instructions.
2. In a pan, heat olive oil and sauté garlic and chili.
3. Add prawns and cook until pink and opaque.
4. Toss in the cooked spaghetti and mix well.
5. Serve with a sprinkle of parsley and a squeeze of lemon juice.

TIPS: Add cherry tomatoes for a refreshing touch.

N.V.: Calories: 320, Carbs: 45g, Protein: 18g, Fat: 9g

LEMON AND OLIVE TAGINE

P.T.: 15 mins

C.T.: 1 HOUR

INGR:

- 4 chicken thighs
- 1 lemon, sliced
- A quarter cup green olives, pitted
- 2 garlic cloves, minced
- 1 tsp ground cumin

PROCEDURE:

1. In a tagine or heavy-bottomed pot, sear chicken thighs until browned.
2. Add garlic, cumin, lemon slices, and olives.
3. Pour in enough water to half-cover the chicken.
4. Cover and simmer on low heat for 1 hour.
5. Serve with couscous or bread.

TIPS: Garnish with fresh coriander and a sprinkle of smoked paprika.

N.V.: Calories: 310, Carbs: 5g, Protein: 24g, Fat: 21g

MEDITERRANEAN ZUCCHINI BOATS

P.T.: 15 mins

C.T.: 25 mins

INGR:

- 4 medium zucchinis, halved lengthwise
- 1 cup cooked quinoa
- 1/2 cup cherry tomatoes, halved
- A quarter cup crumbled feta cheese
- 2 tbsp chopped fresh basil

PROCEDURE:

1. Scoop out the inside of the zucchinis, creating a boat shape.
2. Mix quinoa, cherry tomatoes, feta, and basil in a bowl.
3. Stuff each zucchini half with the quinoa mixture.
4. Bake at 375°F (190°C) for 20-25 minutes or until zucchinis are tender.
5. Drizzle with olive oil before serving.

TIPS: Garnish with additional chopped basil and a sprinkle of black pepper.

N.V.: Calories: 150, Carbs: 20g, Protein: 6g, Fat: 6g

MEDITERRANEAN LENTIL SALAD

P.T.: 10 mins

C.T.: 20 mins

INGR:

- 1 cup dried lentils
- 1 bell pepper, diced
- 1/2 cucumber, diced
- A quarter cup chopped parsley
- 2 tbsp olive oil

PROCEDURE:

1. Cook lentils according to package directions. Drain and cool.
2. Combine lentils, bell pepper, cucumber, and parsley in a bowl.
3. Drizzle with olive oil and toss to combine.
4. Refrigerate for an hour before serving to allow flavors to meld.
5. Serve chilled.

TIPS: Add crumbled feta cheese for added creaminess.

N.V.: Calories: 210, Carbs: 30g, Protein: 12g, Fat: 7g

ROSEMARY LAMB CHOPS

P.T.: 10 mins

C.T.: 15 mins

INGR:

- 4 lamb chops
- 2 garlic cloves, minced
- 2 tbsp fresh rosemary, chopped
- 2 tbsp olive oil
- Salt to taste

PROCEDURE:

1. Mix garlic, rosemary, olive oil, and salt in a bowl.
2. Rub the mixture onto the lamb chops.
3. Grill for 6-7 minutes on each side or to desired doneness.
4. Let rest for 5 minutes before serving.
5. Serve with a side of roasted vegetables.

TIPS: Pair with a red wine for enhanced flavors.

N.V.: Calories: 280, Carbs: 1g, Protein: 24g, Fat: 20g

OLIVE AND TOMATO ORZO

P.T.: 10 mins

C.T.: 20 mins

INGR:

- 1 cup orzo pasta
- 1/2 cup cherry tomatoes, halved
- A quarter cup black olives, pitted and sliced
- 1 garlic clove, minced
- 2 tbsp olive oil

PROCEDURE:

1. Cook orzo according to package instructions. Drain.
2. In a skillet, sauté garlic in olive oil until fragrant.
3. Add tomatoes and olives, cook for 2-3 minutes.
4. Toss the cooked orzo into the skillet, mixing well.
5. Serve warm with grated Parmesan cheese.

TIPS: Add crushed red pepper for a kick of heat.

N.V.: Calories: 230, Carbs: 32g, Protein: 6g, Fat: 10g

MEDITERRANEAN CHICKPEA SOUP

P.T.: 10 mins

C.T.: 30 mins

INGR:

- 2 cups cooked chickpeas
- 1 onion, chopped
- 1 carrot, diced
- 2 garlic cloves, minced
- 4 cups vegetable broth

PROCEDURE:

1. In a pot, sauté onion, carrot, and garlic until softened.
2. Add chickpeas and vegetable broth. Bring to a boil.
3. Simmer for 20-25 minutes.
4. Blend half the soup for a creamier texture and combine.
5. Serve hot with a drizzle of olive oil.

TIPS: Top with crumbled feta cheese and chopped parsley.

N.V.: Calories: 150, Carbs: 24g, Protein: 7g, Fat: 4g

GRILLED EGGPLANT AND MOZZARELLA STACK

P.T.: 10 mins

C.T.: 15 mins

INGR:

- 1 large eggplant, sliced
- 1 ball fresh mozzarella, sliced
- 1 tomato, sliced
- 2 tbsp olive oil
- 2 tbsp balsamic vinegar

PROCEDURE:

1. Brush eggplant slices with olive oil and grill until tender.
2. Stack grilled eggplant with a slice of mozzarella and tomato.
3. Drizzle with balsamic vinegar.
4. Season with salt and pepper.
5. Serve as a light main or side dish.

TIPS: Garnish with fresh basil leaves.

N.V.: Calories: 210, Carbs: 10g, Protein: 8g, Fat: 16g

MEDITERRANEAN FISH EN PAPILLOTE

P.T.: 10 mins

C.T.: 20 mins

INGR:

- 4 fish fillets (like cod or tilapia)
- 1/2 cup cherry tomatoes, halved
- A quarter cup olives, pitted
- 2 garlic cloves, minced
- 2 tbsp olive oil

PROCEDURE:

1. Place each fish fillet on a piece of parchment paper.
2. Top with tomatoes, olives, and garlic.
3. Drizzle with olive oil and season with salt and pepper.
4. Fold parchment paper over fish and seal edges, creating a pouch.
5. Bake at 375°F (190°C) for 20 minutes or until fish is cooked through.

TIPS: Open pouches at the table for a dramatic presentation.

N.V.: Calories: 220, Carbs: 4g, Protein: 25g, Fat: 12g

SPINACH AND FETA STUFFED CHICKEN

P.T.: 15 mins

C.T.: 25 mins

INGR:

- 4 chicken breasts
- 1 cup fresh spinach, chopped
- 1/2 cup crumbled feta cheese
- 2 garlic cloves, minced
- 1 tbsp olive oil

PROCEDURE:

1. Make a slit in each chicken breast to create a pocket.
2. Mix spinach, feta, and garlic in a bowl.
3. Stuff chicken breasts with the spinach mixture.
4. Secure with toothpicks to keep filling inside.
5. Sauté chicken in olive oil until fully cooked, turning occasionally.

TIPS: Serve with a lemon wedge for added zest.

N.V.: Calories: 260, Carbs: 2g, Protein: 30g, Fat: 14g

LEMON HERB COUSCOUS SALAD

P.T.: 10 mins

C.T.: 10 mins

INGR:

- 1 cup couscous
- A quarter cup chopped fresh herbs (parsley, mint, cilantro)
- 1 lemon, zested and juiced
- 2 tbsp olive oil
- Salt and pepper to taste

PROCEDURE:

1. Cook couscous according to package directions. Fluff and cool.
2. Mix in herbs, lemon zest, and juice.
3. Drizzle with olive oil and season with salt and pepper.
4. Toss until everything is well combined.
5. Serve as a refreshing side dish.

TIPS: Add diced cucumber and cherry tomatoes for more freshness.

N.V.: Calories: 210, Carbs: 30g, Protein: 6g, Fat: 8g

GARLIC SHRIMP PASTA

P.T.: 10 mins

C.T.: 15 mins

INGR:

- 200g spaghetti pasta
- 150g raw shrimp, peeled and deveined
- 3 garlic cloves, minced
- 2 tbsp olive oil
- A quarter cup fresh parsley, chopped

PROCEDURE:

1. Cook spaghetti according to package directions until al dente. Drain and set aside.

2. In a skillet, heat olive oil over medium heat. Add garlic and sauté until fragrant.

3. Add shrimp and cook until they turn pink, about 2-3 minutes per side.

4. Toss cooked spaghetti into the skillet, mixing well with the shrimp and garlic.

5. Garnish with fresh parsley before serving.

TIPS: Sprinkle with chili flakes for a spicy kick.

N.V.: Calories: 350, Carbs: 45g, Protein: 20g, Fat: 10g

Chapter 6: Delectable Desserts

CLASSIC BAKLAVA

P.T.: 20 mins

C.T.: 35 mins

INGR:

- 1 pack phyllo dough sheets
- 1 cup mixed nuts (walnuts, pistachios), chopped
- 1/2 cup honey
- 1/2 cup unsalted butter, melted
- 1 tsp ground cinnamon

PROCEDURE:

1. Preheat the oven to 350°F (175°C). Brush a baking dish with melted butter.
2. Layer a sheet of phyllo dough in the dish. Brush with more butter. Repeat this process until you have 5 sheets layered.
3. Mix the chopped nuts with cinnamon and sprinkle half over the phyllo sheets. Add another 5 buttered sheets on top, then the rest of the nuts. Finish with a final layer of 5 more buttered sheets.
4. Cut the baklava into diamond or square shapes using a sharp knife. Bake for 30-35 minutes until golden brown.
5. As soon as baklava is removed from the oven, drizzle the honey evenly over it, allowing it to seep into the cuts.

TIPS: Serve cooled, but not refrigerated.

N.V.: Calories: 180, Carbs: 25g, Protein: 3g, Fat: 8g

ALMOND ORANGE BLOSSOM CAKE

P.T.: 15 mins

C.T.: 25 mins

INGR:

- 200g ground almonds
- 100g sugar
- 2 eggs
- 1 tsp orange blossom water
- Zest of 1 orange

PROCEDURE:

1. Preheat oven to 350°F (175°C) and grease a round cake tin.
2. Mix together ground almonds, sugar, and orange zest in a bowl.
3. Whisk the eggs and blend them into the almond mixture.
4. Add the orange blossom water, stirring until just combined.
5. Pour the batter into the cake tin and bake for 25 minutes or until a knife comes out clean.

TIPS: Dust with powdered sugar before serving.

N.V.: Calories: 250, Carbs: 20g, Protein: 6g, Fat: 16g

FIG AND RICOTTA TARTLETS

P.T.: 20 mins

C.T.: 20 mins

INGR:

- 1 pack ready-made tartlet cases
- 100g ricotta cheese
- 5 fresh figs, quartered
- 2 tbsp honey
- 1 tsp vanilla extract

PROCEDURE:

1. Preheat oven to 350°F (175°C).
2. Mix ricotta cheese with vanilla extract until smooth.
3. Spoon the ricotta mixture into the tartlet cases.
4. Top each tartlet with fig quarters.
5. Drizzle with honey and bake for 20 minutes.

TIPS: Serve with an extra drizzle of honey or chopped pistachios.

N.V.: Calories: 130, Carbs: 15g, Protein: 2g, Fat: 7g

CHOCOLATE DIPPED ORANGE SLICES

P.T.: 15 mins

C.T.: 10 mins

INGR:

- 2 large oranges, thinly sliced
- 150g dark chocolate (70% cocoa)
- Sea salt flakes
- Olive oil
- Zest of 1 orange

PROCEDURE:

1. Place orange slices on a baking sheet lined with parchment paper.
2. In a double boiler, melt the chocolate. Stir in a teaspoon of olive oil to smooth.
3. Dip half of each orange slice into the chocolate and place back on the sheet.
4. Sprinkle with sea salt flakes and orange zest.
5. Allow to set in a cool place for about an hour.

TIPS: Store in the refrigerator to maintain freshness.

N.V.: Calories: 95, Carbs: 12g, Protein: 1g, Fat: 5g

POMEGRANATE JELLY

P.T.: 10 mins

C.T.: 2 HOURS

INGR:

- 2 cups pomegranate juice
- 100g sugar
- 2 tbsp gelatin powder
- A quarter cup cold water
- Seeds of 1 pomegranate

PROCEDURE:

1. Sprinkle gelatin powder over cold water and let it sit for about 5 minutes.
2. In a saucepan, heat pomegranate juice and sugar until sugar is dissolved.
3. Remove from heat, add the gelatin mixture, and stir until gelatin is dissolved.
4. Pour into dessert glasses or molds and sprinkle with pomegranate seeds.
5. Chill in the refrigerator until set, about 2 hours.

TIPS: Serve with a dollop of Greek yogurt on top.

N.V.: Calories: 110, Carbs: 25g, Protein: 2g, Fat: 0g

LEMON AND OLIVE OIL CAKE

P.T.: 15 mins

C.T.: 35 mins

INGR:

- 1 cup flour
- 1/2 cup olive oil
- 1 cup sugar
- 2 eggs
- Zest and juice of 1 lemon

PROCEDURE:

1. Preheat oven to 350°F (175°C) and grease a round cake tin.
2. Whisk together the eggs, sugar, and olive oil until well combined.
3. Gradually add in the flour, mixing just until incorporated.
4. Stir in the lemon zest and juice.
5. Pour the batter into the cake tin and bake for 30-35 minutes.

TIPS: Drizzle with a simple icing made of powdered sugar and lemon juice.

N.V.: Calories: 280, Carbs: 35g, Protein: 3g, Fat: 15g

DATE AND WALNUT TRUFFLES

P.T.: 20 mins

C.T.: 1 HOUR (CHILLING TIME)

INGR:

- 1 cup dates, pitted
- 1/2 cup walnuts
- 2 tbsp cocoa powder
- 1 tbsp honey
- Desiccated coconut for rolling

PROCEDURE:

1. In a food processor, blend dates, walnuts, cocoa powder, and honey until a sticky mixture forms.
2. Using your hands, roll the mixture into small balls.
3. Roll each ball in desiccated coconut.
4. Place truffles in the refrigerator to set for at least an hour.

TIPS: Can be stored in an airtight container for up to a week.

N.V.: Calories: 80, Carbs: 12g, Protein: 1g, Fat: 4g

APRICOT AND ALMOND TART

P.T.: 20 mins

C.T.: 25 mins

INGR:

- 1 ready-made pie crust
- 8 fresh apricots, halved and pitted
- 1/2 cup ground almonds
- 2 tbsp honey
- 1 egg

PROCEDURE:

1. Preheat oven to 375°F (190°C).
2. Spread the ground almonds over the pie crust.
3. Arrange the apricot halves over the almonds.
4. Whisk the egg and honey together and pour over the apricots.
5. Bake for 25 minutes or until the tart is golden brown.

TIPS: Serve with a scoop of vanilla ice cream.

N.V.: Calories: 210, Carbs: 28g, Protein: 3g, Fat: 10g

ROSEWATER PISTACHIO PUDDING

P.T.: 10 mins

C.T.: 2 HOURS (CHILLING TIME)

INGR:

- 2 cups milk
- A quarter cup sugar
- 3 tbsp cornstarch
- 2 tbsp rosewater
- A quarter cup pistachios, chopped

PROCEDURE:

1. In a saucepan, heat the milk and sugar until sugar is dissolved.
2. Mix cornstarch with a little cold water to form a slurry. Add this to the milk while stirring.
3. Keep stirring until the mixture thickens.
4. Remove from heat and stir in the rosewater.
5. Pour into individual serving glasses and refrigerate for 2 hours. Garnish with pistachios before serving.

TIPS: Can be topped with whipped cream for extra richness.

N.V.: Calories: 140, Carbs: 20g,   Protein: 3g, Fat: 6g

HONEY DRIZZLED SEMOLINA CAKE

P.T.: 15 mins

C.T.: 30 mins

INGR:

- 1 cup semolina
- 1/2 cup sugar
- 1/2 cup plain yogurt
- 1 tsp baking powder
- Honey for drizzling

PROCEDURE:

1. Preheat oven to 350°F (175°C) and grease a rectangular cake tin.
2. Mix semolina, sugar, yogurt, and baking powder in a bowl.
3. Pour the batter into the tin and bake for 25-30 minutes or until a skewer comes out clean.
4. Drizzle honey over the hot cake and let it absorb.

TIPS: Cut into squares and serve with a dollop of clotted cream.

N.V.: Calories: 180, Carbs: 30g, Protein: 4g, Fat: 5g

RICOTTA AND HONEY STUFFED FIGS

P.T.: 15 mins

C.T.: NONE

INGR:

- 8 fresh figs
- 1 cup ricotta cheese
- 3 tbsp honey
- Zest of 1 lemon
- A quarter cup chopped walnuts

PROCEDURE:

1. Slice the top off each fig and make a crosswise cut without cutting through the base.
2. Mix ricotta cheese with lemon zest.
3. Stuff each fig with the ricotta mixture.
4. Drizzle with honey and garnish with chopped walnuts.

TIPS: Serve chilled.

N.V.: Calories: 105, Carbs: 16g, Protein: 3g, Fat: 4g

MEDITERRANEAN ALMOND COOKIES

P.T.: 15 mins

C.T.: 12 mins

INGR:

- 1 cup almond flour
- A quarter cup sugar
- 1 egg white
- 1/2 tsp almond extract
- Slivered almonds for topping

PROCEDURE:

1. Preheat oven to 350°F (175°C).
2. Mix almond flour, sugar, egg white, and almond extract until combined.
3. Roll the mixture into small balls and place on a baking sheet.
4. Press an almond sliver into each cookie.
5. Bake for 10-12 minutes or until edges are golden.

TIPS: Store in an airtight container.

N.V.: Calories: 85, Carbs: 7g, Protein: 2g, Fat: 6g

LAVENDER INFUSED CUSTARD

P.T.: 10 mins

C.T.: 20 mins

INGR:

- 2 cups milk
- 4 egg yolks
- A quarter cup sugar
- 1 tsp dried lavender buds
- 1 tsp vanilla extract

PROCEDURE:

1. Heat milk with lavender buds until just below boiling, then remove from heat and let steep for 10 minutes.
2. Whisk egg yolks and sugar until pale.
3. Slowly pour the lavender-infused milk into the yolk mixture, stirring constantly.
4. Return the mixture to the stove on low heat, stirring until it thickens.
5. Strain out lavender and mix in vanilla extract.

TIPS: Chill before serving.

N.V.: Calories: 130, Carbs: 15g, Protein: 4g, Fat: 6g

OLIVE OIL AND CHOCOLATE MOUSSE

P.T.: 20 mins

C.T.: 2 HOURS (CHILLING TIME)

INGR:

- 100g dark chocolate
- 3 eggs, separated
- 3 tbsp olive oil
- 2 tbsp sugar
- Pinch of sea salt

PROCEDURE:

1. Melt the chocolate slowly in a heatproof bowl over simmering water.
2. Once melted, whisk in the olive oil until combined.
3. In another bowl, whisk egg yolks with sugar until creamy. Fold this into the chocolate mixture.
4. Whisk the egg whites with a pinch of salt until stiff peaks form. Gently fold this into the chocolate mixture.
5. Pour mousse into individual serving dishes and refrigerate for 2 hours.

TIPS: Garnish with grated chocolate or a drizzle of olive oil.

N.V.: Calories: 220, Carbs: 15g, Protein: 5g, Fat: 15g

CARAMELIZED PEAR AND ROSEMARY TART

P.T.: 20 mins

C.T.: 30 mins

INGR:

- 1 ready-made pie crust
- 3 pears, thinly sliced
- A quarter cup sugar
- 2 sprigs of rosemary, finely chopped
- 2 tbsp butter

PROCEDURE:

1. Preheat oven to 375°F (190°C).
2. In a skillet, melt butter and add sugar, stirring until it becomes a caramel.
3. Add sliced pears and rosemary, coating them in the caramel.
4. Arrange caramelized pears on the pie crust.
5. Bake for 25-30 minutes or until the crust is golden brown.

TIPS: Serve with a dollop of whipped cream.

N.V.: Calories: 260, Carbs: 35g, Protein: 2g, Fat: 12g

GREEK YOGURT AND BERRIES PARFAIT

P.T.: 10 mins

C.T.: NONE

INGR:

- 2 cups Greek yogurt
- 1 cup mixed berries (strawberries, blueberries, raspberries)
- 3 tbsp honey
- 1/2 tsp vanilla extract
- A quarter cup granola

PROCEDURE:

1. In a bowl, mix Greek yogurt with honey and vanilla extract.

2. In serving glasses, layer Greek yogurt, mixed berries, and granola.

3. Repeat layers until the glass is full, finishing with a layer of berries.

TIPS: Chill for 30 minutes before serving.

N.V.: Calories: 180, Carbs: 25g, Protein: 10g, Fat: 4g

MANDARIN ORANGE AND ALMOND PUDDING

P.T.: 15 mins

C.T.: 3 HOURS (CHILLING TIME)

INGR:

- 2 cups mandarin orange juice
- A quarter cup sugar
- 2 tbsp gelatin powder
- A quarter cup cold water
- A quarter cup chopped almonds

PROCEDURE:

1. Sprinkle gelatin over cold water and let it sit for about 5 minutes.

2. Heat mandarin orange juice and sugar in a pan until sugar dissolves.

3. Remove from heat and add gelatin mixture, stirring until dissolved.

4. Pour into serving dishes, and sprinkle with chopped almonds.

5. Refrigerate for 3 hours or until set.

TIPS: Serve with whipped cream on top.

N.V.: Calories: 130, Carbs: 25g,   Protein: 3g, Fat: 3g

CHIA SEED AND POMEGRANATE PUDDING

P.T.: 10 mins

C.T.: 4 HOURS (CHILLING TIME)

INGR:

- 2 cups almond milk
- 1/2 cup chia seeds
- 2 tbsp honey
- 1 tsp vanilla extract
- 1/2 cup pomegranate seeds

PROCEDURE:

1. Mix almond milk, chia seeds, honey, and vanilla extract in a bowl.
2. Cover and refrigerate for at least 4 hours or until thickened.
3. Before serving, top with pomegranate seeds.

TIPS: Can also be topped with sliced almonds or coconut shreds.

N.V.: Calories: 150, Carbs: 20g, Protein: 4g, Fat: 6g

MEDITERRANEAN CINNAMON ROLL-UPS

P.T.: 20 mins

C.T.: 15 mins

INGR:

- 1 pack puff pastry
- A quarter cup sugar
- 1 tbsp ground cinnamon
- A quarter cup raisins
- A quarter cup finely chopped walnuts

PROCEDURE:

1. Preheat oven to 375°F (190°C).

2. Roll out puff pastry and sprinkle with sugar, cinnamon, raisins, and walnuts.
3. Roll the pastry tightly and cut into 1-inch slices.
4. Place slices on a baking sheet and bake for 12-15 minutes or until golden brown.

TIPS: Serve warm with a dusting of powdered sugar.

N.V.: Calories: 200, Carbs: 25g, Protein: 3g, Fat: 10g

SEMOLINA AND ORANGE BLOSSOM CAKE

P.T.: 15 mins

C.T.: 30 mins

INGR:

- 1 cup semolina
- 1/2 cup sugar
- A quarter cup unsalted butter, melted
- 1 tsp baking powder
- 2 tbsp orange blossom water

PROCEDURE:

1. Preheat oven to 375°F (190°C).
2. In a mixing bowl, combine semolina, sugar, and baking powder.
3. Add melted butter and orange blossom water, and mix until a smooth batter forms.
4. Pour the batter into a greased baking dish and spread evenly.
5. Bake for 25-30 minutes or until golden brown and a toothpick inserted comes out clean.

TIPS: Allow the cake to cool, then cut into diamond shapes and garnish with pistachio nuts.

N.V.: Calories: 210, Carbs: 30g, Protein: 3g, Fat: 8g

LEMON AND ROSEMARY SORBET

P.T.: 20 mins

C.T.: 4 HOURS (FREEZING TIME)

INGR:

- 2 cups water
- 1 cup sugar
- Zest and juice of 2 lemons
- 2 sprigs of rosemary

PROCEDURE:

1. In a saucepan, combine water, sugar, lemon zest, and rosemary. Bring to a boil, then simmer for 5 minutes.
2. Remove from heat and let the mixture steep for 15 minutes. Remove the rosemary sprigs.
3. Add lemon juice to the mixture and stir.
4. Transfer the mixture to a shallow dish and freeze. Every hour, stir the mixture with a fork until it's completely frozen and has a slushy texture.

TIPS: Serve with a sprig of rosemary as a garnish for an elegant presentation.

N.V.: Calories: 80, Carbs: 20g, Protein: 0g, Fat: 0g

1

Chapter 7: Refreshing Drinks and Beverages

LEMON MINT SPRITZER

P.T.: 5 mins

C.T.: 0 mins

INGR:

- Juice of 1 lemon
- 6-8 fresh mint leaves
- 1 cup sparkling water
- 1 tbsp honey
- Ice cubes

PROCEDURE:

1. In a glass, muddle the mint leaves.
2. Add honey and lemon juice and mix well.
3. Fill the glass with ice cubes.
4. Top up with sparkling water and stir gently.
5. Garnish with a lemon slice and a sprig of mint.

TIPS: For a more intense flavor, let the drink sit for a few minutes before serving.

N.V.: Calories: 60, Carbs: 15g, Protein: 0g, Fat: 0g

FIG AND ALMOND MILK SMOOTHIE

P.T.: 10 mins

C.T.: 0 mins

INGR:

- 3 fresh figs
- 1 cup almond milk
- 1 tbsp honey
- 1/2 tsp vanilla extract
- Ice cubes

PROCEDURE:

1. Wash and quarter the figs.
2. In a blender, combine figs, almond milk, honey, and vanilla extract.
3. Blend until smooth.
4. Add ice cubes and blend again until chilled.
5. Pour into a glass and enjoy immediately.

TIPS: Top with chopped almonds for an added crunch.

N.V.: Calories: 150, Carbs: 25g, Protein: 3g, Fat: 5g

HIBISCUS AND ROSE ICED TEA

P.T.: 5 mins

C.T.: 10 mins

INGR:

- 2 hibiscus tea bags
- 2 tsp rose water
- 2 cups boiling water
- 1 tbsp honey
- Ice cubes

PROCEDURE:

1. Steep hibiscus tea bags in boiling water for 5 minutes.
2. Remove the tea bags and let it cool.
3. Stir in honey and rose water.
4. Fill a glass with ice cubes and pour the tea over.
5. Garnish with rose petals.

TIPS: Adjust the sweetness based on preference.

N.V.: Calories: 40, Carbs: 10g, Protein: 0g, Fat: 0g

MEDITERRANEAN SANGRIA

P.T.: 10 mins

C.T.: 0 mins

INGR:

- 1 cup red wine
- 1/2 orange, sliced
- 1/2 lemon, sliced
- 1 tbsp honey
- Sparkling water

PROCEDURE:

1. In a pitcher, combine wine, orange slices, and lemon slices.
2. Add honey and stir until dissolved.
3. Fill glasses with ice cubes.
4. Pour the wine mixture over ice until 3/4 full.
5. Top up with sparkling water and give a gentle stir.

TIPS: Let it sit for an hour for flavors to meld.

N.V.: Calories: 120, Carbs: 15g, Protein: 0.5g, Fat: 0g

POMEGRANATE AND BASIL REFRESHER

P.T.: 5 mins

C.T.: 0 mins

INGR:

- 1 cup pomegranate juice
- 6-8 basil leaves
- 1 cup sparkling water
- 1 tbsp honey
- Ice cubes

PROCEDURE:

1. In a glass, muddle basil leaves.
2. Add honey and pomegranate juice, and stir well.
3. Fill the glass with ice cubes.
4. Top up with sparkling water and stir gently.
5. Garnish with a few pomegranate arils.

TIPS: Use fresh pomegranate juice for the best flavor.

N.V.: Calories: 100, Carbs: 25g, Protein: 0.5g, Fat: 0g

LAVENDER LEMONADE

P.T.: 5 mins

C.T.: 10 mins

INGR:

- Juice of 2 lemons
- 1 tbsp dried lavender buds
- 1 cup boiling water
- 1 tbsp honey
- Ice cubes

PROCEDURE:

1. Steep lavender buds in boiling water for 5 minutes.
2. Strain and let it cool.
3. In a pitcher, combine lemon juice, lavender water, and honey.
4. Stir well until honey dissolves.
5. Serve over ice cubes in glasses.

TIPS: Adjust sweetness based on preference.

N.V.: Calories: 60, Carbs: 15g, Protein: 0g, Fat: 0g

CUCUMBER AND MINT COOLER

P.T.: 10 mins

C.T.: 0 mins

INGR:

- 1 cucumber
- 10 mint leaves
- 1 tbsp honey
- 1 cup water
- Ice cubes

PROCEDURE:

1. Peel and chop the cucumber.
2. In a blender, add cucumber, mint leaves, honey, and water.
3. Blend until smooth.
4. Strain the mixture into a pitcher.
5. Serve over ice cubes in glasses.

TIPS: Perfect for hot summer days.

N.V.: Calories: 40, Carbs: 10g, Protein: 1g, Fat: 0.2g

PEAR AND ROSEMARY MOCKTAIL

P.T.: 5 mins

C.T.: 0 mins

INGR:

- 1 pear, juiced
- 1 sprig rosemary
- 1 tbsp honey
- 1 cup sparkling water
- Ice cubes

PROCEDURE:

1. In a glass, muddle rosemary.
2. Add honey and pear juice, and stir well.
3. Fill the glass with ice cubes.
4. Top up with sparkling water and stir gently.
5. Garnish with a slice of pear.

TIPS: Use fresh pear juice for the best flavor.

N.V.: Calories: 90, Carbs: 22g, Protein: 0.5g, Fat: 0.2g

GRAPEFRUIT AND THYME SPRITZ

P.T.: 5 mins

C.T.: 0 mins

INGR:

- Juice of 1 grapefruit
- 1 sprig thyme
- 1 tbsp honey
- 1 cup sparkling water
- Ice cubes

PROCEDURE:

1. In a glass, muddle thyme.
2. Add honey and grapefruit juice, and stir well.
3. Fill the glass with ice cubes.
4. Top up with sparkling water and stir gently.
5. Garnish with a slice of grapefruit.

TIPS: Perfect for brunch or an afternoon refreshment.

N.V.: Calories: 80, Carbs: 20g, Protein: 0.5g, Fat: 0g

CHERRY AND BASIL FIZZ

P.T.: 10 mins

C.T.: 0 mins

INGR:

- 1 cup cherries, pitted
- 6-8 basil leaves
- 1 tbsp honey
- 1 cup sparkling water
- Ice cubes

PROCEDURE:

1. In a blender, combine cherries, basil leaves, and honey.
2. Blend until smooth.
3. Strain the mixture into a pitcher.
4. Fill glasses with ice cubes, pour the cherry mixture until half full, then top up with sparkling water.

TIPS: Adjust sweetness based on preference.

N.V.: Calories: 70, Carbs: 17g, Protein: 1g, Fat: 0.2g

OLIVE LEAF ICED TEA

P.T.: 5 mins

C.T.: 10 mins

INGR:

- 2 olive leaf tea bags
- 1 tbsp honey
- 2 cups boiling water
- 1 lemon slice
- Ice cubes

PROCEDURE:

1. Steep olive leaf tea bags in boiling water for 5 minutes.
2. Remove the tea bags and let it cool.
3. Stir in honey until dissolved.
4. Serve over ice cubes in glasses with a slice of lemon.

TIPS: Olive leaf tea has a unique flavor and numerous health benefits.

N.V.: Calories: 40, Carbs: 10g, Protein: 0g, Fat: 0g

ORANGE AND ANISE REFRESHER

P.T.: 5 mins

C.T.: 0 mins

INGR:

- Juice of 2 oranges
- 1 star anise
- 1 tbsp honey
- 1 cup sparkling water
- Ice cubes

PROCEDURE:

1. In a glass, muddle star anise.
2. Add honey and orange juice, stirring well.
3. Add ice cubes and top up with sparkling water.
4. Stir gently and serve.

TIPS: The star anise gives a delightful licorice note to the drink.

N.V.: Calories: 80, Carbs: 20g, Protein: 1g, Fat: 0g

FENNEL AND APPLE JUICE

P.T.: 10 mins

C.T.: 0 mins

INGR:

- 1 fennel bulb, juiced
- 1 apple, juiced
- 1 tsp lemon juice
- 1 tbsp honey
- Ice cubes

PROCEDURE:

1. Combine fennel juice and apple juice in a glass.
2. Stir in lemon juice and honey.
3. Add ice cubes and serve immediately.

TIPS: This juice combination is both refreshing and beneficial for digestion.

N.V.: Calories: 100, Carbs: 24g, Protein: 1g, Fat: 0g

APRICOT AND ROSEMARY COOLER

P.T.: 10 mins

C.T.: 0 mins

INGR:

- 2 apricots, pitted and juiced
- 1 sprig rosemary
- 1 tbsp honey
- 1 cup sparkling water
- Ice cubes

PROCEDURE:

1. Muddle rosemary in a glass.
2. Add honey and apricot juice, stirring well.
3. Add ice cubes and top up with sparkling water.
4. Stir gently and serve.

TIPS: Apricots provide a naturally sweet flavor, reducing the need for added sugars.

N.V.: Calories: 70, Carbs: 18g, Protein: 0.5g, Fat: 0g

PERSIMMON AND GINGER TONIC

P.T.: 10 mins

C.T.: 0 mins

INGR:

- 1 ripe persimmon, juiced
- 1-inch ginger, juiced
- 1 tbsp honey
- 1 cup sparkling water
- Ice cubes

PROCEDURE:

1. Combine persimmon and ginger juices in a glass.
2. Stir in honey until dissolved.
3. Add ice cubes and top up with sparkling water.
4. Stir gently and serve.

TIPS: This drink offers a sweet and spicy kick, making it unique and refreshing.

N.V.: Calories: 80, Carbs: 20g, Protein: 0.5g, Fat: 0g

ROSE WATER ICED TEA

P.T.: 5 mins

C.T.: 10 mins

INGR:

- 2 black tea bags
- 2 tsp rose water
- 2 cups boiling water
- 1 tbsp honey
- Ice cubes

PROCEDURE:

1. Steep black tea bags in boiling water for 5 minutes.
2. Remove the tea bags and let it cool.
3. Stir in honey and rose water.
4. Serve over ice cubes in glasses.

TIPS: This drink offers a floral twist to the traditional iced tea.

N.V.: Calories: 40, Carbs: 10g, Protein: 0g, Fat: 0g

TANGERINE AND BASIL SPRITZ

P.T.: 5 mins

C.T.: 0 mins

INGR:

- Juice of 2 tangerines
- 6-8 basil leaves
- 1 tbsp honey
- 1 cup sparkling water
- Ice cubes

PROCEDURE:

1. Muddle basil leaves in a glass.
2. Add honey and tangerine juice, stirring well.
3. Add ice cubes and top up with sparkling water.
4. Stir gently and serve.

TIPS: Tangerines offer a sweeter and tangier flavor than regular oranges.

N.V.: Calories: 80, Carbs: 20g, Protein: 1g, Fat: 0g

DATE AND YOGURT SMOOTHIE

P.T.: 10 mins

C.T.: 0 mins

INGR:

- 5 dates, pitted
- 1 cup yogurt
- 1 tbsp honey
- 1/2 tsp cinnamon
- Ice cubes

PROCEDURE:

1. Combine all ingredients in a blender.
2. Blend until smooth.
3. Pour into a glass and enjoy immediately.

TIPS: Dates provide natural sweetness, so you can adjust the amount of honey based on your preference.

N.V.: Calories: 230, Carbs: 48g, Protein: 5g, Fat: 3.5g

LIME AND MINT ICED TEA

P.T.: 5 mins

C.T.: 10 mins

INGR:

- 2 green tea bags
- Juice of 1 lime
- 6-8 mint leaves
- 1 tbsp honey
- 2 cups boiling water

PROCEDURE:

1. Steep green tea bags in boiling water for 3 minutes.
2. Remove the tea bags and let it cool.
3. Stir in honey, lime juice, and add mint leaves.
4. Serve over ice cubes in glasses.

TIPS: This drink offers a refreshing blend of flavors, perfect for warm days.

N.V.: Calories: 40, Carbs: 10g, Protein: 0g, Fat: 0g

KIWI AND LAVENDER SMOOTHIE

P.T.: 10 mins

C.T.: 0 mins

INGR:

- 2 kiwis, peeled
- 1 tsp lavender buds
- 1 cup yogurt
- 1 tbsp honey
- Ice cubes

PROCEDURE:

1. Combine all ingredients in a blender.
2. Blend until smooth.
3. Pour into a glass and enjoy immediately.

TIPS: The lavender adds a delicate floral note, making this smoothie stand out.

N.V.: Calories: 200, Carbs: 42g, Protein: 5g, Fat: 3g

CUCUMBER & BASIL REFRESHER

P.T.: 10 mins

C.T.: 0 mins

INGR:

- 1 large cucumber, peeled and sliced
- 5-6 fresh basil leaves
- 1 tbsp honey (optional)
- 1 liter sparkling water
- Ice cubes

PROCEDURE:

1. In a pitcher, muddle cucumber slices and basil leaves to release their flavors.
2. Add honey if you like it a bit sweeter, and mix well.
3. Add ice cubes to glasses and pour the muddled mixture till it's half full.
4. Top up with sparkling water.

TIPS: For a twist, add a splash of lime or lemon juice.

N.V.: Calories: 30, Carbs: 7g, Protein: 0.5g, Fat: 0.1g

PEAR & THYME SPRITZER

P.T.: 7 mins

C.T.: 0 mins

INGR:

- 1 cup pear juice (freshly pressed if possible)
- 2-3 sprigs of fresh thyme
- 1 cup sparkling water
- 1 tsp lemon juice
- Ice cubes

PROCEDURE:

1. Muddle thyme sprigs at the bottom of a glass to release the flavor.
2. Add pear and lemon juices.
3. Add ice cubes to the glass.
4. Top with sparkling water and give it a gentle mix.

TIPS: Garnish with a thin pear slice and a thyme sprig for a chic presentation.

N.V.: Calories: 70, Carbs: 18g, Protein: 0.3g, Fat: 0.2g

CITRUS & LAVENDER INFUSION

P.T.: 8 mins

C.T.: 0 mins

INGR:

- 1/2 lemon, sliced
- 1/2 orange, sliced
- A quarter tsp dried culinary lavender or 1 fresh lavender sprig
- 1 liter still water
- Ice cubes

PROCEDURE:

1. In a pitcher, place lemon and orange slices.
2. Sprinkle in the dried lavender or place the fresh sprig.
3. Add still water and let it infuse for a few minutes.
4. Serve in glasses over ice.

TIPS: Letting the infusion sit for a longer period intensifies the flavors.

N.V.: Calories: 25, Carbs: 6g, Protein: 0.4g, Fat: 0.1g

Chapter 8: 28 Days of Mediterranean Meal Plans

Week 1 Mediterranean Meal Plan:

Day	Breakfast	Lunch	Dinner	Dessert	Beverage
1	Mediterranean Chickpea Soup	Seafood Paella	Mediterranean Chicken Thighs	Classic Baklava	Lemon Mint Spritzer
2	Greek Yogurt And Berries Parfait	Olive And Tomato Orzo	Grilled Lamb Koftas	Almond Orange Blossom Cake	Hibiscus And Rose Iced Tea
3	Semolina And Orange Blossom Cake	Roasted Red Pepper Hummus Bowl	Lemon And Olive Tagine	Fig And Ricotta Tartlets	Pomegranate And Basil Refresher
4	Ricotta And Honey Stuffed Figs	Mediterranean Lentil Salad	Spinach And Feta Stuffed Tomatoes	Chocolate Dipped Orange Slices	Fig And Almond Milk Smoothie
5	Greek Yogurt Tzatziki Dip With Veggies	Lemon Herb Couscous Salad	Aubergine (Eggplant) Parmigiana	Pomegranate Jelly	Mediterranean Sangria
6	Mandarin Orange And Almond Pudding	Mediterranean Zucchini Boats	Garlic And Chili Prawn Pasta	Date And Walnut Truffles	Grapefruit And Thyme Spritz
7	Chia Seed And Pomegranate Pudding	Olive Tapenade Crostini With Salad	Spinach And Ricotta Cannelloni	Lavender Infused Custard	Cucumber & Basil Refresher

Week 2 Mediterranean Meal Plan:

Day	Breakfast	Lunch	Dinner	Dessert	Beverage
8	Mediterranean Cinnamon Roll-Ups	Fresh Tomato Bruschetta With Salad	Rosemary Lamb Chops	Honey Drizzled Semolina Cake	Pear And Rosemary Mocktail
9	Lemon And Rosemary Sorbet	Easy Mediterranean Cucumber Salad	Herb-Infused Sea Bass	Ricotta And Honey Stuffed Figs	Olive Leaf Iced Tea
10	Mediterranean Shrimp Cocktail	Zucchini And Mint Fritters	Mediterranean Stuffed Peppers	Apricot And Almond Tart	Cucumber And Mint Cooler
11	Greek Yogurt Tzatziki Dip With Veggies	Garlic Shrimp Pasta	Grilled Eggplant And Mozzarella Stack	Rosewater Pistachio Pudding	Orange And Anise Refresher
12	Date And Yogurt Smoothie	Cherry Tomato And Basil Skewers With Orzo	Spinach And Feta Stuffed Chicken	Mediterranean Almond Cookies	Fennel And Apple Juice
13	Lime And Mint Iced Tea	Quick Marinated Artichokes With Bread	Lemon And Olive Tagine	Caramelized Pear And Rosemary Tart	Persimmon And Ginger Tonic
14	Kiwi And Lavender Smoothie	Spicy Lemon Hummus With Veggies	Mediterranean Zucchini Boats	Olive Oil And Chocolate Mousse	Tangerine And Basil Spritz

Week 3 Mediterranean Meal Plan:

Day	Breakfast	Lunch	Dinner	Dessert	Beverage
15	Semolina And Orange Blossom Cake	Spinach And Feta Stuffed Mushrooms	Aubergine (Eggplant) Parmigiana	Fig And Ricotta Tartlets	Rose Water Iced Tea
16	Cucumber & Basil Refresher	Lemon And Rosemary Olives	Seafood Paella	Greek Yogurt And Berries Parfait	Grapefruit And Thyme Spritz
17	Spinach And Ricotta Cannelloni	Olive Tapenade Crostini	Mediterranean Chickpea Soup	Mandarin Orange And Almond Pudding	Fig And Almond Milk Smoothie
18	Chia Seed And Pomegranate Pudding	Mediterranean Lentil Salad	Roasted Red Pepper Hummus Bowl	Lavender Infused Custard	Pear & Thyme Spritzer
19	Lemon Herb Couscous Salad	Garlic And Chili Prawn Pasta	Mediterranean Fish En Papillote	Chocolate Dipped Orange Slices	Hibiscus And Rose Iced Tea
20	Aubergine And Yogurt Spread	Baked Falafel Bites	Spinach And Feta Stuffed Tomatoes	Classic Baklava	Citrus & Lavender Infusion
21	Mediterranean Shrimp Cocktail	Simple Feta Cheese Dip With Veggies	Mediterranean Chicken Thighs	Pomegranate Jelly	Cherry And Basil Fizz

Week 4 Mediterranean Meal Plan:

Day	Breakfast	Lunch	Dinner	Dessert	Beverage
22	Mediterranean Cinnamon Roll-Ups	Zucchini And Mint Fritters	Rosemary Lamb Chops	Caramelized Pear And Rosemary Tart	Orange An Anise Refresher
23	Kiwi And Lavender Smoothie	Easy Mediterranean Cucumber Salad	Olive And Tomato Orzo	Ricotta And Honey Stuffed Figs	Lime And Mint Iced Tea
24	Spinach And Feta Stuffed Chicken	Fresh Tomato Bruschetta	Herb-Infused Sea Bass	Mediterranean Almond Cookies	Persimmo And Ginge Tonic
25	Mediterranean Zucchini Boats	Cherry Tomato And Basil Skewers	Lemon And Olive Tagine	Almond Orange Blossom Cake	Date And Yogurt Smoothie
26	Lemon And Rosemary Sorbet	Quick Marinated Artichokes	Grilled Eggplant And Mozzarella Stack	Honey Drizzled Semolina Cake	Apricot An Rosemary Cooler
27	Garlic Shrimp Pasta	Spicy Lemon Hummus With Pita	Grilled Lamb Koftas	Olive Oil And Chocolate Mousse	Cucumbe And Mint Cooler
28	White Bean And Rosemary Stew	Mediterranean Stuffed Peppers	Mediterranean Lentil Salad	Lemon And Olive Oil Cake	Fennel An Apple Juic

Conclusion

Reflecting on the Mediterranean Journey: Insights and Personal Growth

It's a well-known adage that life is about the journey, not the destination. The same rings true for our culinary explorations, especially when we traverse the rich landscapes of the Mediterranean region. At the start of this adventure, one might have viewed the Mediterranean diet as merely a collection of recipes from diverse regions, but as we progress, we uncover that it is so much more. It's a tapestry of cultures, histories, and stories, told through the lens of food.

This journey is not just about tasting new flavors, but also about understanding and appreciating the centuries of traditions, the dedication of generations of cooks, and the sheer love and passion for food that the Mediterranean people possess.

The Symphony of Ingredients

The Mediterranean diet does not just toss random ingredients together; it is a symphony. It's about understanding how the sharpness of feta cheese contrasts beautifully with the sweetness of a ripe tomato, or how the bitterness of olives can be tempered with the soft, buttery texture of fresh bread. There's an art and science to these pairings. It's the reason why every bite we took made us feel connected, not just to the land but to the people and their traditions.

Every meal is a reminder of sun-drenched olive groves, azure coastal lines, bustling local markets, and the gentle hum of life in Mediterranean towns and cities. This experience transcends beyond taste. It's about understanding that every dish has a story, every ingredient has a history, and every meal is a testament to the spirit of the Mediterranean people.

A Personal Odyssey

As we dove into the nuances of this diet, it was evident that it wasn't just a dietary transformation but also a personal one. The slow-cooked stews taught us patience. The intricate pastries, a lesson in dedication. The varied tapas, a testament to the joy of community and sharing.

The act of cooking, which may have once been viewed as a mere chore, transforms into an act of love, meditation, and creativity. The kitchen metamorphoses from a mundane space to an artist's studio, where ingredients become paints, and the plate, a canvas.

Beyond the Plate

The insights gained go beyond culinary skills. Understanding the Mediterranean diet is also a lesson in sustainability, balance, and harmony. It's about acknowledging that the earth gives us its bounty, and in return, we respect it by using sustainable practices, wasting less, and understanding the true value of what we consume.

This journey compels one to become not just a consumer, but a caretaker — of our bodies, our traditions, and our environment.

Culinary Wisdom: More than Just Recipes

While recipes provide a structure, the true essence of the Mediterranean diet lies in the wisdom passed down through generations. It's the understanding that food is not just fuel, but medicine. It's the belief that a meal is not just about satiation, but celebration.

And as we assimilate this wisdom, we evolve not just as cooks, but as individuals. We begin to value quality over quantity, tradition over trend, and community over convenience.

Continuing the Mediterranean Adventure: Tips for Lifelong Adherence

When we speak of the Mediterranean lifestyle, it is crucial to understand that it's not a fad diet or a temporary phase; it's a lifelong journey. It's about embracing a way of life that has thrived for centuries, embodying its principles into our daily routines, and passing them on for generations to come. While we've delved deep into the Mediterranean's culinary wonders, it's equally vital to integrate this diet into our lives in a way that feels organic and sustainable.

Finding Your Rhythm

While the Mediterranean diet offers a template, it's up to each individual to tailor it to their unique lifestyle, preferences, and cultural nuances. The beauty of this diet is its adaptability. Whether you're a seasoned chef or someone venturing into the culinary world, there's room for personalization.

Remember, the core of this diet is balance. It's not about stringent restrictions, but about finding harmony in what you eat, ensuring you get a mix of nutrients, flavors, and textures.

Seasonal and Local: The Twin Pillars

One of the secrets behind the vibrancy of Mediterranean cuisine is its reliance on fresh, seasonal, and locally sourced ingredients. Adopting this principle doesn't just amplify the taste but also ensures you get the maximum nutritional benefits.

By prioritizing local produce, you support local farmers and reduce your carbon footprint. It's a practice that not only benefits your health but also aids the environment and the local economy.

Engaging the Senses

The Mediterranean way of life is not just about the food on your plate, but the experience surrounding it. It's about engaging all your senses. From the vibrant colors of the dishes, the tantalizing aroma wafting through the kitchen, the texture of fresh bread, to the melodic sounds of sizzling and simmering. It's a holistic experience.

Remember to savor each meal. Take the time to appreciate the intricacies, the craftsmanship that went into creating each dish. This not only enhances your culinary experience but also fosters mindfulness and gratitude.

Building a Mediterranean Community

At the heart of the Mediterranean lifestyle is a strong sense of community. Meals aren't just about nourishment; they're social gatherings, a time to bond with family and friends. Try to incorporate this communal aspect. Host potlucks, share recipes, or even start a cooking club. When the diet is experienced as a shared journey, adherence becomes more effortless and enjoyable.

Embracing the Mediterranean Mindset

Beyond the cuisine, adopting the Mediterranean mindset is about appreciating the simpler joys of life. It's about taking a stroll in nature, enjoying a siesta, or just basking in the sun. It's this combination of diet, activity, and mindfulness that constitutes the true essence of the Mediterranean lifestyle.

Celebrating Small Wins

Like any journey, there will be challenges along the way. But instead of getting deterred, celebrate the small wins. Maybe it's mastering a new recipe, discovering a new ingredient, or just the sheer joy of a meal well cooked. These moments of joy compound over time and keep you motivated.

Lifelong Learning

The Mediterranean region is vast, and its culinary landscape, diverse. Even as you integrate this diet into your life, remain a student. Continually explore, experiment, and evolve. The world of Mediterranean cuisine is vast and waiting for you to delve deeper.

Appendix

Further Resources: Books, Courses, and Culinary Tours

The Mediterranean region's rich tapestry of history, culture, and cuisine is vast and varied. While our journey has provided an in-depth exploration, there's always more to discover. For those hungry for more knowledge, here are some seminal books that delve deep into the Mediterranean lifestyle:

- **"The Mediterranean Diet for Beginners" by Charlie Stewart**: A comprehensive guide that offers a step-by-step approach for those new to the diet. Stewart elucidates the health benefits and provides weekly meal plans to kickstart the Mediterranean journey.

- **"Mediterranean Harvest: Vegetarian Recipes from the World's Healthiest Cuisine" by Martha Shulman**: For vegetarians looking to embrace the Mediterranean diet, Shulman's book is a treasure trove. With over 500 recipes, it's a testament to the diet's versatility.

- **"Mediterranean Clay Pot Cooking" by Paula Wolfert**: An ode to traditional Mediterranean cooking techniques, Wolfert explores the magic of clay pot cooking, a method that brings out the rich flavors and textures of the ingredients.

- **"A Culinary History of the Mediterranean" by David Gentilcore**: For history buffs, this book offers a chronological journey through the Mediterranean's culinary evolution, tracing its influences from various cultures and eras.

Courses That Embark on a Culinary Adventure

For hands-on learning, nothing beats a dedicated course that offers both theoretical knowledge and practical skills. Here are some reputed courses that provide an immersive Mediterranean culinary experience:

- **The Mediterranean Culinary Academy**: Located in the heart of Malta, this academy offers courses ranging from beginner to advanced. With a focus on sustainable and local ingredients, it provides a holistic understanding of the diet's ethos.

- **Cucina Mazzini's Mediterranean Cooking Course**: This Florence-based culinary school offers short-term courses focusing on traditional Mediterranean dishes. Students get a chance to visit local markets, understand ingredient selection, and cook under the guidance of seasoned chefs.

Culinary Tours: A Gastronomic Journey

There's no better way to understand a cuisine than to immerse oneself in its native environment. Culinary tours offer an unparalleled experience of tasting authentic dishes, understanding local food practices, and learning from local chefs.

- **Greek Gastronomic Odyssey**: A week-long tour that takes participants through the heart of Greece. From olive groves to vineyards, from bustling Athens markets to serene island getaways, it's a feast for the senses.

- **Spanish Culinary Trails**: Explore the Spanish countryside, dive into the world of tapas, and indulge in the rich wines of the region. This tour is a celebration of Spain's culinary heritage.

- **Moroccan Culinary Expedition with Chef Ali**: Journey through the bustling markets of Marrakech, explore the Atlas mountains, and learn the secrets of traditional Moroccan dishes with the renowned Chef Ali.

Glossary of Culinary Terms: A Mini-Dictionary for the Budding Chef

- **Aubergine**: Another term for eggplant, a nightshade vegetable common in Mediterranean dishes, often roasted, grilled, or turned into spreads.
- **Baklava**: A rich dessert originating from the Ottoman Empire, made of layers of filo pastry, filled with chopped nuts and sweetened with syrup or honey.
- **Canneloni**: Tubular pasta that is typically stuffed with filling, often including ingredients like ricotta and spinach, then baked.
- **Crostini**: Small toasted bread slices, typically served with various toppings as an appetizer or snack.
- **Falafel**: Deep-fried balls made from ground chickpeas, herbs, and spices, commonly served in Middle Eastern dishes.
- **Gastronomic**: Pertaining to the art and knowledge involved in good food and drink.
- **Hummus**: A creamy spread or dip made from blended chickpeas, tahini, lemon juice, and garlic.
- **Koftas**: Meatballs or meat skewers, often made of lamb or beef, seasoned with various spices and herbs.
- **Lentil**: A type of legume, frequently used in Mediterranean soups and stews.
- **Moussaka**: A baked dish, originating from Greece, layered with aubergine, meat (often lamb), and topped with béchamel sauce.
- **Orzo**: Rice-shaped pasta, often used in soups or as a side dish.
- **Paella**: A traditional Spanish rice dish, cooked in a large shallow pan, often with saffron, vegetables, and various meats or seafood.
- **Ricotta**: A creamy, white Italian cheese, commonly used in pasta fillings, desserts, or as a spread.
- **Sangria**: A Spanish-origin alcoholic beverage made from red wine, fruit, and sometimes spirits or soda.
- **Tagine**: Both a North African clay pot with a conical lid and the stew-like dish cooked within it, often containing meat, dried fruits, and spices.

- **Tapas**: Small appetizers or snacks, native to Spanish cuisine, ranging from olives and cheeses to more elaborate dishes.
- **Tzatziki**: A Greek sauce or dip made from yogurt, cucumber, garlic, and dill.
- **Umbra**: Refers to the shady side of a hill, often where certain Mediterranean vineyards are located for optimal grape growth.
- **Vineyard**: A plantation of grapevines, especially one producing grapes for winemaking.
- **Zucchini**: Known in some parts of the world as courgette, it's a type of summer squash, frequently found in Mediterranean dishes.
- **Semolina**: Coarse wheat flour, used in making pasta and some Mediterranean desserts.
- **Risotto**: An Italian rice dish, cooked until creamy with broth and often flavored with various ingredients like saffron, seafood, or vegetables.
- **Couscous**: A North African dish of small steamed wheat granules, served as a side or with stews.
- **Glossary of Culinary Terms**: Small, oven-baked savory pastries filled with meat, cheese, or vegetables.
- **Gastronomic**: Pertaining to the art and knowledge involved in good food and drink.
- **Mint**: A fragrant herb, commonly used in Mediterranean dishes and beverages.
- **Rosemary**: An aromatic shrub with needle-like leaves, often used as a culinary herb in Mediterranean cooking.
- **Tagine**: A slow-cooked Moroccan stew, traditionally made in a clay pot of the same name.
- **Culinary**: Of or related to cooking or the kitchen.
- **Pomegranate**: A fruit bearing shrub or small tree, the seeds of which are used in numerous Mediterranean dishes and drinks.
- **Lavender**: A fragrant herb with purple flowers, used in some Mediterranean recipes for its aromatic properties.

- **Basil**: An aromatic herb, frequently used fresh in recipes and closely associated with Italian cuisine.
- **Sautéing**: Cooking food quickly in a small amount of oil over direct heat.
- **Simmering**: Cooking food gently in liquid just at or below the boiling point.
- **Culinary Tours**: Organized trips with a focus on exploring the food and cooking of a particular region.
- **Culinary Academy**: An institution focused on the study and practice of cooking and food preparation.

Acknowledgments: Extending Gratitude to Contributors

The journey of bringing this book to fruition was not taken alone. Along the winding roads of the Mediterranean, from its azure shores to its verdant hills, many have played instrumental roles in ensuring that the essence of this rich culinary landscape was captured accurately and vividly. This acknowledgment section, though just a few paragraphs long, is a heartfelt ode to those unsung heroes who have illuminated this endeavor with their expertise, insights, and unwavering support.

To the chefs and home cooks from Spain to Greece, Italy to Morocco, and all the lands in between, whose kitchens I was privileged enough to step into: your generosity in sharing family recipes, secret techniques, and stories by the stove is the backbone of this book. You opened your homes and hearts, showcasing the spirit of the Mediterranean - a spirit of warmth, hospitality, and shared meals. Every page of this book is infused with the flavors and tales you've generously shared.

A sincere thank you to the team of researchers, food historians, and dieticians who ensured the information presented is not only appetizing but also accurate and beneficial. Your meticulous attention to detail and relentless pursuit of truth were invaluable, ensuring that readers get a genuine and comprehensive view of the Mediterranean diet and lifestyle.

To the editing and publishing team: your patience, guidance, and unwavering belief in this project transformed a dream into a tangible reality. Through late-night revisions, brainstorming sessions, and the intricacies of layout designs, you've been the silent architects shaping this creation.

A special note of gratitude to the countless local farmers, fishers, and market vendors: you are the unsung heroes of the Mediterranean. It's your dedication and hard work that brings the freshest ingredients to our tables, ensuring that the dishes retain their authenticity and flavor.

Lastly, to you, the reader. Your curiosity about the Mediterranean world, your eagerness to dive into its culinary wonders, and your trust in this guide are the very reasons for its existence. This book is an invitation, a shared journey, and it's your participation that makes it truly special.

Measurement Conversion Table

Volume Measurements

US Measurement	Metric Measurement
1 tsp (tsp)	5 milliliters (ml)
1 tbsp (tbsp)	15 milliliters (ml)
1 fluid ounce (fl oz)	30 milliliters (ml)
1 Cup	240 milliliters (ml)
1 pint (2 Cs)	470 milliliters (ml)
1 quart (4 Cs)	0.95 liters (L)
1 gallon (16 Cs)	3.8 liters (L)

Weight Measurements

US Measurement	Metric Measurement
1 ounce (oz)	28 grams (g)
1 pound (lb)	450 grams (g)
1 pound (lb)	0.45 kilograms (kg)

Length Measurements

US Measurement	Metric Measurement
1 inch (in)	2.54 centimeters (cm)
1 foot (ft)	30.48 centimeters (cm)
1 foot (ft)	0.3048 meters (m)
1 yard (yd)	0.9144 meters (m)

Temperature Conversions

Fahrenheit (°F)	Celsius (°C)
32°F	0°C
212°F	100°C
Formula: (°F - 32) x 0.5556 = °C	Formula: (°C x 1.8) + 32 = °F

Oven Temperature Conversions

US Oven Term	Fahrenheit (°F)	Celsius (°C)
Very Slow	250°F	120°C
Slow	300-325°F	150-165°C
Moderate	350-375°F	175-190°C
Moderately Hot	400°F	200°C
Hot	425-450°F	220-230°C
Very Hot	475-500°F	245-260°C

Made in the USA
Columbia, SC
30 October 2024